Indexing Theory, Indexing Methods and Search Devices

by

Frederick Jonker

The Scarecrow Press, Inc.

New York & London   1964

This work was performed under the sponsorship of the Information Research Division of the Air Force Office of Scientific Research by Jonker Business Machines Inc. of Gaithersburg, Maryland, under contract AF-49 (638)961.

The section dealing with indexing methods as well as the section dealing with the information retrieval devices are based on a revision and expansion of earlier papers written by the author while employed at Documentation, Inc. This work was likewise sponsored by the Air Force Office of Scientific Research.

PREFACE

Commercial application of I.R. (Information Retrieval) is still in its infancy. The infancy has been full of controversy. Dispute about the merits of indexing systems and claims and counterclaims for competing hardware have abounded. While the I.R. industry continues development of a galaxy of devices, each of which seems only to add to the state of confusion, the professionals in the art have begun to agree on a number of basic principles and general conclusions. Using these as a foundation, we have attempted to erect the framework of a theory of Information Retrieval.

It seems doubtful that there can ever be a single theory of information retrieval. I.R. is not a science; it is an "art" that can be divided into different and, to an extent, independent areas.

1. Indexing

2. Coding

3. Search Devices.

Coding is by far the simplest of these three problems. The general principles of coding are well understood from communications theory. Coding will, therefore, not be discussed in this study.[1]

However, we have attempted to establish the outline of a theory of indexing, as well as the outline of a theory of search devices.

The theory of indexing divides into two different aspects, the theory of index terminology, discussed in Chapter I and the theory of indexing methods, discussed in Chapter II. Chapter III discusses the interrelationships of these two theories. The last Chapter is devoted to the fundamental principles of search devices.

1. Casey, R. S., "Punched Cards", Reinhold Publishing Co., 1958.

Stiassny, S., "Mathematical Analysis of Various Superimposed Coding Methods", Am Doc, 11, No. 2 (April, 1950).

Table of Contents

Introduction

General   11

The Effect of Search Equipment Upon Retrieval
    Theory   13

Definition of "Item of Information"   19

Definition of Indexing   20

Definition of Index Data   20

Definition of "Search Process"   22

Chapter I   Theory of Index Terminology

The Structure of Index Language   23

The Mechanism of Growth and the Expension of
    Language

The "Terminological Continuum"   24

Evolution of Terminology   27

Artificial Terminology as "Itensified" Colloquial
    Terminology   31

Index Terminology and the Terminological
    Continuum   34

The Possibility of a "Universal Index
    Terminology"   40

Practical Use of the Tool of the Terminological
    Continuum   47

Chapter II   Theory of Indexing Methods

General Remarks   51

History and Analysis of the Information
  Control Problem   51

General Theory of Indexing Methods, The
  "Connective Continuum"   67

Selection of Position in the Continuum   80

Chapter III   Integration of Continua

Connection Between "Terminological Continuum"
  and "Connective Continuum"   81

Chapter IV   Basic Principles of
                 Information Retrieval Devices

The Nature of a Theory of I. R. Devices   85

Limitation of Present Treatment of the Problem   86

Definition of Information Retrieval Machines   87

Primary Design Considerations   90
    A.   Store Organization or "Grouping"
               Conventional Grouping
               Inverted Grouping
    B.   Searching of the Index Data (matching)
    C.   Arrangement for Store Access

Secondary Design Considerations   115
    A.   Coding Principles
    B.   Structural Considerations
               Form of "bit"
               Form of Record
    C.   Microphotographic Document Storage

Summation of Examples of 8 Basic Systems   119

References   122

List of Illustrations

Figure 1	25
Figure 2	26
Figure 3	26
Figure 4	26
Figure 5	56
Figure 6	57
Figure 7	59
Figure 8a, b, c	69
Figure 8d, e, f,	70
Figure 8g, h, i, j,	71
Figure 8k	72
Figure 9	79
Figure 10	83
Figure 11	90
Figure 12	91
Figure 13	93
Figure 14	94
Figure 15	94
Figure 16	95
Figure 17	97
Figure 18	98
Figure 19	99
Figure 20	99
Figure 21	100
Figure 22	102
Figure 23	103
Figure 24	104
Figure 25	105
Figure 26	106
Figure 27	110
Figure 28	112
Figure 29	113

Introduction

General

The Importance of the Indexing Problem

The determination of the particular coding and machine system that will best suit the requirements of any particular problem, is basically a matter of engineering judgment. Ultimately it reduces to problems of cost. Almost any compatible combination of coding and machine systems can, in principle, perform any required form of information search. However, some machines may be better suited to a particular information control problem than others. The "best" system is simply that with the lowest total cost for the information entry and search operations to provide the required results.

The validity of cost as the ultimate criterion is not limited to machine problems. All problems in information retrieval can ultimately be reduced to one single factor, cost -- how to deliver a specified quantity, quality and speed of service at the lowest possible cost. All "improvements" in this field, and many other fields, basically aim at one thing and that is lowering of the total cost of a system that will provide specified performance.

Mechanization is commonly assumed to be the answer to this problem. However, the cost of indexing, the intellectual work of assigning descriptive "terms" to an item of information, is usually very much higher than the cost of the clerical work of entering the data into the system or the cost of an adequate machine retrieval system.

For example, the cost of indexing a collection of 10,000 documents may vary from $50,000 to $150,000. The cost of entering the data into a search system need not exceed $5,000. Mechanical devices to search such a collection are available for about the same cost as that of entering the data.

Therefore, mechanization can be a partial answer only. The other part of the answer must be found in systems of indexing that provide adequate quality of indexing at lower cost. It is this consideration that gives the problem of indexing its tremendous importance.

The Need for Generalized Treatment of the Problem

The various systems of indexing in use today confront us with a picture of conflicting claims. Rather than single out and discuss their differences, we will attempt the opposite and look for elements which these apparently conflicting systems have in common, and, will then attempt to establish a single "general" theory.

The suspicion that such a general theory must exist seems to find confirmation in the pattern of evolution of many of the sciences, particularly the physical sciences. Fields of science usually start with the

observation and measurement of a number of newly
discovered phenomena which are vaguely felt to be related. As the science progresses, closer and closer
relationships between these phenomena are discovered.
Finally a generalized theory and generalized equations
become possible. Many sciences which do not lend
themselves to quantification exhibit basically the same
pattern of development. The evolution of a science
always seems to progress from the understanding of a
large number of relationships, each linking a limited
number of phenomena,to a single relationship relating
all observed phenomena.

The conclusion seems to be that no true understanding of existing indexing systems and problems
seems possible unless all indexing systems can be seen
in the light of more general common precepts which
link all of them into a single "closed" system.

The present theory of indexing methods actually is
an expansion of an earlier theory of indexing (see "The
Descriptive Continuum, a Generalized Theory of Indexing." AF-OSR TN 57-287; ASTIA AD 132358)

The Effect of Search Equipment Upon Retrieval Theory
There are two general approaches to mechanization of Information Retrieval. One is based on item
grouping and the other is based on term grouping.

In item grouping all documents or, in more general terms, all items of information, are searched
linearly one by one. The records are generally dedicated to items of information and the terms describing

13

these are encoded on the item-records.

In term grouping the records are dedicated to terms, each term used in the system having its own record. The items are identified by serial numbers, and the term-records have the serial numbers of items encoded on them.

The first approach is the reverse of the second, but both methods perform basically the same function. Anything that can be performed by complex search functions by the one approach can somehow also be done by the other approach. These facts have by now gained general recognition and indexing methods may be considered generally to be independent of retrieval equipment.

Earlier thinking on indexing and retrieval theory was greatly influenced by the use of linear search equipment. The logical consequences of this use were:

1. No sharp distinction was made between the storage of the information or its abstract or extract on the one hand and the storage of index data on the other hand. (For example, the Western Reserve University machine scans the abstracts.)

2. All special or complex search functions comprising logical sums, products and differences and syntactical relationships are "programmed" into the search machines. Because of the analogy with computer logic, Boolean algebra became accepted as the mathematical model

14

for I.R.

In recent years the opposite form, based on term-grouping, has gained more general acceptance for machine searching. Users of this type of equipment have come to make the following adjustments in their thinking:

1. They came to look upon the information storage or the storage of the abstracts as something distinctly different from the search mechanism. All that is stored in the search mechanism is the "index data." It alone is used by most retrieval machines.

2. Logical sums and differences and combinations of these can all be reduced to logical products. For example, using Uniterm systems or systems based on optical coincidence of term cards, a logical sum of terms A and B can be made simply by reading the postings on the term cards of term A and B sequentially and writing them on the same piece of paper. Of course, certain numbers will appear in duplicate, but this in no way impairs the practicality of the approach. Logical differences, for example, between term A and B can be made by reading out term A and then term B and deleting the readings of the term A appearing on the list of term B. Thus logical sums and differences do not, from the standpoint of information retrieval

15

machinery, seem to be separate search functions. In fact they require no machinery at all. They are simply "Readout" functions. On the other hand, the making of logical products or search by coincidences of terms does appear to require a mental process or a piece of equipment.

3. Syntactical relationship too can be reduced simply to coincidence of terms. Take, for example, the problem of a document having information on brass, bird, cages and brown, dog, houses. Here the terms brass, bird and cage on the one hand, and brown, dog, and house on the other hand should be linked together to prevent "false coordinations." However, the same result can be accomplished by splitting this document into two different items of information and giving each one its own serial number. These are linked together outside of the search equipment in the information store.

Then there is a whole category of syntactical problems that could be lumped together in the catch-all category of "roles." Sometimes the same word can have many different meanings, depending on context and proximity or connection with other terms. Actually nearly all of these problems are caused by the fact that, unlike most other languages, English does not generally express grammatical differences by differences in spelling. In languages of Latin or Germanic origin the forms of a word differ greatly, and whether they are used as verbs, nouns, adverbs or adjectives is expressed in the way they are spelled. We need not only to recognize the terms "blind" and "Venetian," but to recognize each as two different terms, one, the noun and the other, the adjective. By giving each a separate code or term card, we can in a search distinguish between "Venetian blinds" and "blind Venetians." In the same way we can distinguish between two entirely different meanings of the same word, such as, for example, "tanks" as containers and as military vehicles, etc.

4.   Generic relationships. If we wish to make generic searches, the generic relationships we wish to recognize can be noted in the access guide or thesaurus. This is a list of the terms with scope notes and other information, such as generic relationships to other terms. For example, with the term "dog" we might find the notation: "Subclass of canines. Comprises the classes of retrievers, police dogs, and sled dogs." With the term "retriever" we will then find the notation: "Subclass of dogs, which is subclass of

canines."

If we intend to make frequent generic searches, a term could be entered by itself (as found in the text of the document), plus all of its higher generic levels. This procedure simplifies the search but greatly increases the input labor.

It is also possible to enter only the term itself (as taken from the text) and if generic searches are required, to find all of the lower classes to be searched in the Access Guide. The sum of these (see below) then provides the answer. This procedure reduces the cost of data input and preserves the flexibility of adding, changing or eliminating generic relationships, but greatly increases the output cost.

At this point the following conclusion seems justified:

Mechanized I.R. may be looked upon simply as performance of search by coincidence of terms. This function is the heart of I.R. equipment. More complex search functions may be considered a combinations of readout functions and search by coincidence of terms. All syntactical and generic relationships can be built into the access guide, the vocabulary of index terms.

Uniterm systems of coordinate indexing, superimposable card systems, punched card collating systems, punched card computers, and magnetic tape systems based on term records, computer systems based on random access memories, which in all account for about ninety per cent of all I.R. installations, now solve their logical problems completely or nearly completely along the lines discussed above.

Thus looking upon the I.R. art purely from the point of view of mechanized searching, it would seem logical to attempt to base a theory of information retrieval upon intersection of terms alone (also known as coordination of terms or coincidence of terms). Yet in practice it is hard to distinguish between mechanized and non-mechanized I.R. (The search by coordination based on the Uniterm Card System is the prime example.) Besides, in practice the older systems based on a classification or a subject heading list system and mechanized systems are so interwoven that a general theory should encompass both.

The theory of indexing methods, which will be developed in subsequent sections, will show that most actual systems are based on a combination of coordination and hierarchy. It will also show that systems based largely on coordination will usually employ a form of mechanical coincidence device. The theory will further show that the intersective and hierarchical relationships are basically identical, with hierarchy a special case of intersection.

Definition of Item of Information
Definition of the term "indexable item" is prereq-

uisite to establishment of a theory of indexing. The delineation of the item may frequently seem arbitrary; the indexable item may be a book or chapters of a book or pages or paragraphs. However, when we index, we isolate coherent "closed" sections and define these as our items. Thus a travel journal dealing with the crossing of rivers in Africa, the treatment of snakebites by witchdoctors in Africa and the hunting habits of the Bushman in Africa will be treated as three separate items, each with a separate item number. The only index term these items would have in common would be Africa.

It is this "coherence" among terms that converts them into an "item of index data." An item of index data actually is a "concept" compounded from a number of concepts. The nature of the coherence or compounding process will later be examined in detail.

Definition of Indexing

Indexing is the art of assigning one or more terms to an "item of information" so as to characterize it. The word "term" is used here in its broadest sense and comprises any form of class, subclass, subject heading, single word or combinations of words.

Definition of Index Data

Information Retrieval systems do not deal primarily with the item of information itself; they deal with the so-called Index Data. Index data are stored in the I.R. memory and are scanned and manipulated in each search. The information collection may be stored in the same physical equipment of it may be stored in separate equipment. I. R. equipment uses only index data in performing its search.

The index data may be a telegraphic representation or abstract of the complete item, in which redundancy has been reduced. It is all the I. R. system "knows." Thus every "item of information" in the information collection is represented in the I. R. system by an "item of index data. We use the terms "index data" and "item of index data" because a number of terms selected from a predetermined vocabulary represent data rather than information in the generally accepted sense of these terms.

Every item of index information must, of course, contain all the important concepts contained in the item of information. In the item of information the terminology for these concepts occurs along with terms, such as "with," "including," "at," "from," "after," and many others, indicating various relationships among these concepts. Other relationships are based on proximity of words, their order, etc. In the I. R. art these are reduced to a few simple relationships, the so-called logical relationships, relationships which a machine can easily recognize. This reduction has become a cornerstone of the I. R. art.

Thus an "item of index data" consists of a number of terms (each representing a concept) and the relationships among these terms.

Definition of Search Process

The I.R. system will not generally accept the form of language in which the request for information originates. The search question has to be phrased in the same language in which the items of index data have been phrased. This formalized language may be close to the living language or it may be a completely artificial language, an index language designed to overcome the ambiguities of living language.

If the interrelations between index terms in the items of index data, as well as the interrelations between the search terms are ignored, the search operation becomes very simple; the search terms are compared with each of the items of index data in the I.R. systems to find those which include the search terms.

This study explores the nature of formalized index languages, the functions they perform and their relationship to living language.

Chapter I: Theory of Index Terminology

The Structure of Index Language

In ideographic languages, such as Chinese, the written symbol and the spoken word have the same meaning, but the written symbol does not show how to pronounce the spoken word.

Most modern languages are "idiophonic." That is to say, the written language is based on the spoken language and there is supposed to be a correspondence between the sounds of the spoken word and the letter of the written word. There generally is a symbol (letter) for every sound and a sound for each individual symbol.

Early languages dealt with only a fraction of the concepts in modern language. As civilization progressed new concepts were being formed and new terminology was created to describe these concepts. The industrial revolution greatly accelerated this process. The present scientific revolution will heighten the pace still more. Knowledge of the process of expansion of language is, therefore, an important requirement for the understanding of the I.R. art.

Generally speaking, a new concept is at first always described by means of a number of older concepts. The term for this new concept is generally a compound term made up of "older" terms, and its meaning is generally narrower than that of the older concepts.

The names of these new concepts, in turn, become the building blocks for the names of newer concepts. For instance, the term "bookcase" and the term for the "knock-down" principle have been connected, with the term "knockdown bookcase" as a result.

This process can go on practically indefinitely. For example, "metal knockdown bookcases" is a narrower term than "knockdown bookcases."

As this process continues, concepts will finally begin to approach a complete item of index data. For example, "drop-testing, knockdown metal bookcase" could be the complete item of index data of a test report on drop tests carried out on a knockdown bookcase made of metal. Thus there is no basic difference between "items of index information," "search questions" and "index terms." They can all be looked upon simply as concepts, or terms.

From the above analysis it will be clear that if initially all new terminology is made up of older terminology, there is potentially a continuum of terminology extending from the letters of the alphabet to the complete items of information.

The "Terminological Continuum"

The "terminological continuum," is schematically shown in Figs. 1, 2 and 3.

A "search question" can be looked upon simply as

a concept or a "term" having its place somewhere in the continuum.

Going from left to right in this continuum, the number of "terms" increases from 26 to a potentially unlimited number, namely, the size of the information collection (see Fig. 2). On the other hand, while the "size" of each term increases, its meaning decreases from almost infinity at the left hand side, to unity at the right hand side; since the item of information is the largest compound term we recognize in an I.R. system, the extent of its meaning will be considered to be unity.   (see Fig. 3)

The I.R. art was defined very broadly as the matching (comparing) of the search-terms against the index-terms of an item of information, to ascertain whether the search terms are included in the item of index information.   This is basically searching for one narrow term defined by a larger number of given wider terms.   Following this definition, the I.R. art can be represented as a movement from left to right along this terminological continuum, or simply as a direction (see Fig. 4).

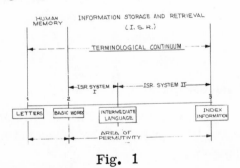

Fig. 1

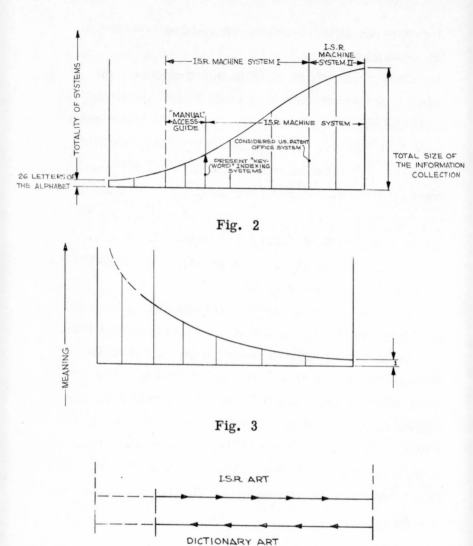

Fig. 2

Fig. 3

Fig. 4

Conversely, the Dictionary Art involves searching for
a number of wider terms defining a given narrower term.
It can, therefore, be represented by movement in the opposite directions (see Fig. 4).

26

It is possible to recognize different "levels" of language, each corresponding to approximate points in the terminological continuum. To use a simple example, when somebody describes a given airplane as: "an arrow-shaped thing that flew in the sky so fast that I could not hear it coming," he is obviously operating close to point 2 in Figure 1 using only the simplest basic concepts like "arrow," "flying," "thing," "fast," "hearing." An expert describing this plane as "a Delta-wing supersonic plane," is using much more complex concepts and is operating somewhere between points 2 and 3 in Figure 1.

Evolution of Terminology

As language grows, the meaning of older terms becomes broader and broader. Simultaneously, narrower new terms are being formed. At first then, new concepts will be described in terms of old concepts. Practically all terms of this type, when first used, start out as two words. Long usage will finally fuse these two words into one and cause them to be considered and spelled as one term, as happened to the words "bookcase" and "aircraft."

This unification process is, however, quite arbitrary, and such long established terms as "water turbines" are still written as two words while "steamturbines" and the much newer word "gasturbines" are frequently written as one. Moreover, the English language is much slower than other languages in accepting long established two-worded "terms" as one. Take, for example, the term "cole slaw." Neither the word "cole" nor the word "slaw" has any meaning in English. Certainly as a concept they belong together. Yet they are mostly still spelled as two separate words.

This lack of consistency presents one of the important sources of the confusion that besets the I.R. art. The

27

aerodynamic expert will insist that "boundary layer control" or even "suction boundary layer control" are concepts and should be treated as one word. The layman has no way of knowing whether these terms constitute standard terminology or not.

The problem of which terms to consider indivisible and which not, is a perplexing one. It will be discussed further in the last section of this book.

Lack of system in the English language is, therefore, the source of many of the problems of the I.R. art. On the other hand, hyper-systemization cannot provide an ultimate answer either. Orderliness is a well known German national characteristic. However, in the Third Reich, standardization of terminology coupled with "purification" of the language by eliminating all non-"Teutonic" words became a mania. The Third Reich simply bristled with mile-long, compound-word terminology, forming a sort of telegraphic description of the concept. However, this functional terminology soon became too long and involved and too hard to remember, and provided a clear indication that absolute parallelism between language and concept cannot be the ultimate solution to the problem of expanding language.

Terms made in this manner by compounding concepts will be referred to as Functional terminology, because it tries to describe the new concept by its functions.

We too have some of these problems. The ear, nose and throat specialist is professionally known as an Otorhinolaryngologist (oto = ear; rhino = nose;

laryn = throat). This may be pronounceable and memorizable by the professional, but the layman or professional in related fields has trouble with it. As a result, the term E.N.T. is gaining acceptance.

One alternative to excessively long or hard-to-remember compounding is the creation of new non-functional words, such as "cybernetics" and "radar" and "automation." There may be some correspondence between the concepts and the syllables of terms, but this correspondence is not essential. The term does not pretend to describe the concept. This will be referred to as Non-Functional terminology.

In terms of the terminological continuum (Figure 1) the language situation can be seen as follows: moving from left to right starting at point 1, the point of basic words, there is, over a certain distance, a parallelism between the name of a new concept and the older terms used to describe the newer concept. This is the area in which new terms are compounded from older terms. However, at a certain distance from point 2 this continuity may at a certain moment be broken when new non-functional terms are being formed.

These new terms are, in a sense, again basic. They are indivisible. Professional language in a highly specialized field may consist largely of such non-functional terminology.

Only when terms of this nature become generally accepted in everybody's everyday language will they become true basic words and be located at point 2.

29

Thus the terminological continuum is not static. More-over, it will be very hard to describe this continuum even at a particular time because it varies from individual to individual.

This means that we can not speak of the "average" terminological continuum. Instead, when designing a particular I. R. system, it should be designed for the terminological continuum of the average user. Take, for example, the design of an I. R. system for electronic engineers which, in addition to dealing with electronic matters, borders on other arts, such as aerodynamics, etc. In this case all indivisible professional electronic terms will be considered basic words, but aerodynamic terms will be to the right of these, somewhere toward the middle of the continuum. The intermediate language or machine language of this I. R. system will comprise all professional terminology in the field of electronics but only the most basic and generally known aerodynamic terminology.

To compound the confusion, the specialist operating in one particular field frequently neglects intensification of older terms. Take, for example, the term "noise." Originally it simply meant undesirable audible vibration, like traffic noise and noise of playing children. However, many other arts use this term, and in sematic communication "noise" is used to mean redundancy. Wireless communications uses the term as "atmospheric" noise. The I. R. art recognizes "retrieval" noise (un-wanted search results, mixed in with the desired results).

Artificial Terminology As "Intensified" Colloquial Terminology

There are many elements in common between the field of communications and I.R. One of the most important of these is the area of terminology.

Verbal communication usually has sufficient context to make communications possible without precise terminology. In indexing, on the other hand, redundancy and context have been removed, and more exact terminology is required.

For example, the word "tank" is too vague for indexing use. Moreover, it has different and unrelated meanings. Only by adding other words is it possible to distinguish among these meanings. For example, in the terms "gasoline tank" and "tank circuit" and "tank tracks," these meanings are distinguished. However, even these concepts are still ambiguous: the "gasoline tank" could actually be an armored vehicle driven by a gasoline engine, and a "U.S. Army tank" could actually be a gasoline container, and a tank circuit could be a route.

"Artificial index language" is intended to provide a separate symbol (word or code) for every important concept. In developing such a language, the first step is, of course, to speak no longer of "tanks" but of "containers" or "armored vehicles" or "electronic tank circuits." However, armored vehicles is still a very general term and distinction must be made between "track-laying armored vehicles" and "wheeled armored vehicles." Since the words "track-laying armored vehicle" are too long for everyday use or for use in I.R. devices, they could be given functional names, such as "armvictrac" or "armvicwheel" or non-functional names like "bloob."

This, then, is a form of artificial index language. It has a much larger number of terms than the living language, and as a result each term is much narrower. There is a one-word name for every important concept. The artificial index language can, therefore, be represented as a point on the terminological continuum (see Figures 1, 2 and 3). It is simply a more intensified language. As such, it is not unique. The same process can be observed operating spontaneously in the living language.

The aircraft industry provides an example of this. Here the word "engine" or "aircraft engine" came to cover too great a variety of different types of engines, so that new terms had to be created. For example, gas turbines which drive propellers are termed "turboprop engines," while gas turbines which transfer all energy to the exhaust jet are termed "turbojet engines." This terminology, originally in use only within the aircraft industry is now found in general usage.

The process of creation of new terms for new concepts that are continuously being born is, of course, never completed. For example, given both piston engines and gas turbines for tank propulsion, it may become desirable to distinguish between "turboarmvic-tracs" and "pistonarmvictracs," etc., or, more properly, "armvictrac-piston" and "armvictrac-turbo."

It seems that the need for precise professional language and the need for precise index terminology are basically identical. The standardized professional terminology and the artificial index terminology are created by the same process.

The spontaneous intensification of a language as a whole proceeds almost imperceptibly. However, there are specialized fields in which a great deal of intensification has taken place. In these fields many new concepts have been formed and named. This sort of language is only spoken by the experts and is unfamiliar to the layman. If the layman has to express himself in this field, he would have to use simple, everyday "unintensified" language. Instead of using the word "turboarmvictrac," he might say "a tank with caterpillar tracks and a gas turbine engine."

While this spontaneous intensification may be adequate to serve the need for a professional language, it is too slow to meet the urgent needs of the I.R. field, because I.R. techniques for finding information have most value when the discoveries are still new and before a generally accepted terminology for the discoveries has been developed. The best solution would be to encourage each profession or discipline to standardize terminology as rapidly as new concepts are created.

We can use standardized professional language for

indexing purposes. The question remains whether it is possible to create an artificial language that is more suitable for indexing purposes than is a professional language. This question will be treated in the section titled "The Possibilities of Universal Index Terminology."

Index Terminology and the Terminological[1,2] Continuum

I. R. devices will generally be applied to specialized information collections. Moreover, they will generally be intended for use by experts or people aspiring to become experts. As a specialized information system intended mostly for experts, an I. R. system, as a rule, requires the use of the special professional language or jargon used in that field. The ideal case would be to have a fully up-to-date professional language which has a standardized term for each important concept in use in that field. In the ideal case every indexer or user of the I. R. system would be an expert and thus speak and understand this professional language. In that case no particular difficulties would be experienced.

In practice, this is never the case. The indexers doing the data input frequently are not sufficiently familiar with its language, and many people who are not fully qualified and who will not be able to phrase their search questions in the professional language, will be using the system.

The strength of a chain is determined by the weakest link. Any I. R. system must, therefore, be able to operate with less than the best trained indexers while users who are less than fully qualified experts will have to be able to use the system.

These requirements pose a real problem. Basically it is the problem of going from the less intensified language of the indexer and lay-user to the more intensified professional language of the I.R. system. It is the problem of going from left to right in the continuum. In other words, it is an I.R. problem.

If this is true, every I.R. system must basically consist of two systems: Subsystem I, going from the lay or informal language to the professional or formal language; and subsystem II, going from the professional language to the items of index information.

In most I.R. systems we will at first glance only be able to recognize the last system. The reason is that the subsystem I is usually atrophied to the point where it is hardly recognizable as an I.R. system. Closer examination will, however, reveal the presence of two distinct systems.

Generally in a mechanized I.R. system, subsystem II will be the machine system and subsystem I will be what could best be termed an Access Guide, a "look-up means" to look up the machine language. Sometimes this access guide will be no more than an alphabetic listing of the terms used in the system.

A categorization of this listing of terms may, in some cases, provide a somewhat more sophisticated and usable "access guide," but usually the categories are not mutually exclusive and will have a certain amoung of overlap.

Categorization is actually a form of classification. In many cases categorization or classification will be extremely difficult and an access guide along the principles of the subject heading list will be more practical.

Generally the access guide will not be a mechanical device and one of the non-mechanical forms of I.R. systems as discussed above will preferably be used. Many of such I.R. systems are basically not complete since they do not possess one of the most important capabilities of an I.R. system, namely, searching by coincidence of two or more terms. However, since, in most systems the distance in the terminological continuum between the user's everyday language and the professional language used in the I.R. system is small, the use of non-mechanical systems for the first subsystem may be quite adequate.

There are, however, cases where subsystem I, as well as subsystem II, will be or should be a full-fledged mechanized I.R. system. Literature on chemical manufacturing processes involving organic chemicals is one possible example. Here the terminology used for organic compounds is so complicated that a mechanical I.R. system may be justified. A search of such a literature collection would start at subsystem I, which is entered with a description of certain compounds in terms of rings and numbers of molecules of certain kinds. The output of this subsystem is names of compounds. Subsystem II is then entered with the names of the compounds plus a number of other terms. It yields the items of information describing the required manufacturing processes as output.

The U.S. Patent Office released data regarding a steroid compound I.R. system on punched cards.[3] Documentation, Inc. prepared a paper on a study comparing the above steroid I.R. system with an optical coincidence search system in which the same data have been entered.[4]

Either of these systems correspond to subsystem I. As visualized by the Patent Office, the outputs of this steroid compound system could be used as the input of a mechanized I.R. system that searches for patents pertaining to these compounds, which latter I. R. system would be subsystem II.

This steroid-compound I.R. system is only one very specialized aspect of the general Patent Office problem, which is a most unusual case, and will, therefore, be briefly discussed as an example of the application of our theory. The reason is that according to the U.S. patent law, patentability is based on "structure" and not on uses. Thus any indexing to be performed in connection with a modernization and possibly a mechanization program will have to be based on structural differences and similarities.

Unfortunately, practically all names of devices and components of devices are based on uses, applications and other attributes, rather than their structure. The term piston engines is one example. The fact that that type of engine has pistons is admittedly part of the structural description. However, it is entirely inadequate as a total description of the structure.

As a result, there is, generally speaking, very little terminology to describe "structures" (in the widest sense of the word, involving shape, as well as movement) with anywhere near the detail and accuracy required for Patent Office purposes.

The Patent Office has, therefore, been experimenting with a structural "language" and code for the description of structures. Since this will in all probability not be a spoken language, only a code without pronounceable and memorizable terms will be required. Let us take, for example, the word "mounting" or "mounted." There are an almost infinite number of different ways that parts can be mounted; they can be rigidly mounted, yieldingly mounted (by spring elements) or movably mounted. Each of these methods of mounting can be broken down a number of ways. For example, movably mounted parts can be mounted to allow for either rotating movement or straight movement. Each of these can again be one dimensional or two dimensional, etc. Each of the innumerable ways of mounting a part should be clearly visualized and described in precise language in a few paragraphs, but a standardized practical terminology of concise terms does not yet exist. The Patent Office has, therefore, been experimenting with a structural code for these purposes.

The look-up problem of this terminology is, of course, a full-fledged I.R. problem. For example, to find the code for a particular method of mounting, terms like "mounting," "rotating one-dimensional," "sliding," "two-dimensional," etc. will have to be entered into I.R. subsystem I. The output will be the correct term or code for this type of mounting. A number of terms obtained in this manner will then be entered into subsystem II, which will give patents as output.

In the example of the Patent Office problem both subsystems may have to be mechanized, but either of the two, in particular, system I, could be a classification system.

It is interesting to observe what happens at the extreme end of the terminological continuum, for example, for the case of the Patent Office. As we move to the right, the standardized terms increase in number (and become narrower in meaning). Terms can thus become so detailed that a patent can be covered by one term only. In that case, subsystem II would disappear. However, the price we pay for operating at this end of the terminological continuum is fantastic. It would mean that in establishing the artificial structural language, we would be preinventing all of the billions of possible structures. We would have to do all this before even the first item (patent) could be entered into the system. After that is done, of course, the entry of patents would be easy, with a unique place for every patent. However, considering the astronomical cost of establishing subsystem I, it will be best to stay at a considerable distance from this end of the continuum, thereby limiting the specificity and number of terms.

At the left side of the terminological continuum, the I.R. system uses the simplest possible language, so that the system can be addressed in the same language, and subsystem I is not needed.

These extreme points of the continuum will hardly ever be used, but most systems will be closer to the left side than to the right side of the terminological continuum.

The Possibility of a "Universal Index Terminology"

A "Universal Index Terminology," to encompass all of the arts and sciences, has been subject to considerable speculation and work for almost a century.

The fact that new terms are frequently composed of older terms gives rise to the question of whether it would be possible to create a universal nomenclature by means of this compounding process.

To make such terminology universal, compounding rules would have to be developed which could be equally applied to all fields of science or industry.

These rules would basically be rules for indexing each concept by a number of terms and putting these terms together into one word. Thus the rules would have to define the point of view from which each concept would be indexed and would have to indicate the hierarchy between these points of view so that we would know in which sequence to place the index terms in compounding them into the new universal terms.

These problems are basically the problems of creating a hierarchical classification (more specifically, an "unpermuted multiple-criterion classification." This subject is discussed in great detail in the next section: "Theory of Indexing Methods.)

It has been noted that the name of a new concept is mostly composed of the names of older concepts, and that such names could sometimes be considered fairly correct but could at other times be basically incorrect. The reason is that when the names are applied, the true nature of the newly discovered concept is frequently not fully known.

For example, automobiles were at first called "horseless-carriages." This name was based only on certain attributes of the object and conveyed little of the inner nature of the thing. In time this name became so pointless that it was superseded by the name "motor car" and later by "automobile." This points up the fact that compound names are frequently based on very trivial attributes.

Although an "airplane" or "airbubble" are both members of the class of "things having to do with air," this is a trivial fact and implies no relationship of

41

any practical significance. The only significant relationship that exists is that they share the word "air." The same applies to the terms "airplane" and "planer" (a woodworking machine to operate on flat pieces of wood). The two have nothing in common that could conceivably put them in the same class from a technical point of view. All these concepts have in common are their symbols -- letters, syllables or words which are used to describe them.

Proponents of a universal index terminology have felt that this lack of systematicity is what is wrong with the living language and that a consistent artificial terminology is needed.

The first question is, of course, what consistent criteria such a nomenclature will have to be based on. The answer generally agreed upon is that "use" is the most universal indexing criterion available. (Most I. R. problems concern technological products and the criterion of use applies to all of these.) Thus it is argued that this form of nomenclature would fit into a classification system. In this approach a clock could, for example, be called a "time-measurer" and a thermometer, a "temperature-measurer." An electric clock would then be a "time-measurer-electric" or in code something like "ti-meas-elec." (Note that "electric" refers to the construction and no longer to use, and that the criterion of "use" quickly become ambiguous.)

There are a great many conditions under which

terminology of this nature can and should be used. The military establishments of practically all nations utilize a terminology based on very much the same principles (see the example of "tanks" given above.) However, instead of being based on the criterion of "use" alone, this standardization is based on a larger number of criteria of particular importance to the military, such as special characteristics of the armament, the wheels or tracks, the engine, the fuel it uses, the weight-class of the vehicle, its speed-class, etc. In making up these terms, the criteria are used in the sequence that military men consider most suited for their particular purposes.

This type of language can, of course, serve as an intermediate language (the machine language or index language). The advantage of the use of this terminology instead of the living language is that subsystem I can now become a classification system and need not be a machine system.

In other cases the special terminology appears to be simply standardization of colloquial terminology. In practice, standardization of terminology in any given field has been tailored to the needs of that particular field, and based on indexing criteria of particular importance to that field, only; and, generally, "use" is the least important of the criteria observed.

We can, for example, name engines after their various uses: automobiles, boats, aircraft, lawn-mowers, etc. However, most technological literature revolves around research and development problems instead of use. From the research and development point of view all these types are similar and division by "use" serves very little purpose. Furthermore such terminology already exists in many fields and it does not seem to have solved I.R. problems.

We can, therefore, conclude that a universal nomenclature based on "use" alone might be possible, but that such a nomenclature would, so far as I.R. purposes are concerned, generally not be specific enough to serve any useful purposes.

It is frequently said that besides "use" there is another universal criterion, namely, "structure." Objects like a tumbler or a pencil which have a simple structure could use nomenclature based on this structure. Other objects may have a structure that is quite complex and their nomenclature can, therefore, be based on only one or two structural characteristics and not on all of them. The choice of the characteristics to be used in structural description then becomes an arbitrary matter.

In internal combustion engines, for example, structural nomenclature might be based on the number of cylinders, the sort of fuel used (for example, "high octane engine") the valve configuration (for example, an "L-head engine") the configuration of the engine block (for example, a "V-engine") etc. If only one of these criteria can be used, an arbitrary choice has to be made. This choice may suit some but may be unsuited to many other fields.

If we want to use more than one criterion, we will have to attribute a hierarchy to these criteria to determine the sequence in which the terms will be placed in the new compound term.

Thus we can conclude that "use" and "structure" are no more than two broad categories, each encompassing a multitude of indexing viewpoints. Since there is no universal viewpoint, there appears to be no basis for maintaining that universal index language is possible.

Special nomenclature can be created. The requirements and the mechanism of creation of special index nomenclature and special nomenclature for professional communication are basically identical. In both cases the nomenclature is based on viewpoints and on hierarchical subordination between these viewpoints that has particular meaning for the discipline concerned.

Points of view and hierarchy may vary greatly even within a narrow field. For example, in military weapons the term "armvictrac-piston" is based on the following viewpoints and sequence: military attribute, general use, propulsion means, power source. The term "turbojet fighter" is based on power source, propulsion system and military attribute. The fact that it is a plane was left out of the nomenclature.

This indicates that it has not, in the past, been possible to create a classification for the terminology of a particular field of science, let alone one for universal classification. Thus it seems that each field of science must develop its own standardized terminology. Problems will, of course, occur at the interfaces of various disciplines, because basically identical concepts may be used in each in an entirely different manner and must, therefore, receive a different name. For example, an automobile hubcap and the lid of a paint can are similar in construction, and they are taken off and mounted in the same manner. These problems can, in principle, be solved by conventional cross referencing techniques which merge vocabularies of narrow but related disciplines into a consolidated vocabulary for a larger discipline.

Practical Use of the Tool
Of
The Terminological Continuum

While on the one hand it is clear that the terminological continuum is real, it is extremely difficult to identify "levels of language" or to determine "the terminological continuum of the average user."

This notion should, therefore, be considered simply a tool to increase our understanding of the I.R. art and its language problems.

The simplest systems, which do not exhibit any particular language problems, are systems where the generators of the information (the authors of the items of information), the indexers and the users of the collection all belong to the same profession or practice the same art and thus use the same professional language. In that case the professional terms found in the text become the index terms, and the index terms may simply be taken from the text. This procedure can be followed in many special library collections. The Uniterm system of coordinate indexing is designed around this procedure. Systems of automatic mechanical indexing[5] are based on similar procedures. This procedure probably promises a breakthrough in the indexing art.

Many users of the Uniterm system carry simpli-

cation beyond this point. In order to reduce the required apparatus (the number of Uniterm cards), terms
like "centrifugal pump," "brake shoe," etc. are broken
up and only Uniterm cards on the individual word "centrifugal," "pump," "brake" and "shoe" are used despite
the fact that they may not by themselves be retrieval
terms. The term "shoe" under which "brake shoes,"
"football shoes" and "horse shoes," etc. might conceivably be posted is obviously of little use by itself
as a retrieval term, so that search questions must always be phrased as bound terms, such as "centrifugal
pumps" and "brake shoes." There is a recognizable
level of index language in any system.

We have seen that, given a narrow field of special-
ization, when the users as well as the indexers are
equally skilled in the professional vernacular in which
the items of information are written and in indexing
methods, no access guide (subsystem I) is required.
However, employing lay indexers or opening the collection to lay users would require the addition of an access guide.

In more general terms the problem is discrepancy
of language level among the generators of the material
(the authors), the indexers and the users of the collection. Thus if a special information collection for
"cross-fertilization" of other arts contains material
written in the highest level of professional language,
the indexer would do well to use a more popular intermediate language in order to make the collection ac-

cessible to the experts in other fields.

A few words to sum up the question of divisibility or indivisibility of terms:

It has been shown that indivisibility is a matter of familiarity with the terms and depends upon the terminological continuum of the user. This is demonstrated by the question of whether or not inversion of compound terms is felt to be necessary.

Large organizations which develop their own tooling have to develop nomenclature (for internal use) for this tooling. The same applies to the components of the products they are manufacturing. Since it is for internal use only, this terminology is frequently extremely informal or just plain sloppy. Other companies in the same type of business may develop a different nomenclature for the same notions. As certain of these notions become public property, terminological confusion sets in. Frequently even within the same organization, different terminology may be developed for the same notions. When consolidation of information becomes necessary these differences become important, and the organization realizes that it has an I.R. problem.

References

1. Perry, J.W., Berry, M.M. and Kent, Allen, "Machine Literature Searching VI. Class Definition and Code Construction," Am Doc, 5, No. 4: 238-44.

"Information Analysis for Machine Searching," Am

49

Doc, 1, No. 3: 133-39 (1950).

Perry J.W., and Kent, A., "Tools for Machine Literature Searching," Interscience Publishers, 1958.

Melton, John L., "The Semantic Code Today," Am Doc, 13, No. 2 (April, 1962).

2. Taube, Mortimer, "Meaning and Linguistic Structures," Studies in Coordinate Indexing, IV, chap. II, Documentation, Inc., Bethesda, Md.

3. Frome, J. and Leibowitz, J., "A Punched Card System for Searching Steroid Compounds," Patent Office R. and D. Report No. 7 (July 8, 1957).

4. Miller, E., Ballard, D., Kingston, J. and Taube, M., "A Comparison of Conventional Grouping and Inverted Grouping of Codes for the Storage and Retrieval of Chemical Data," Air Force - O.R.S. TN, 58-366; A.S.T.I.A. Doc AD 154 272.

5. Newman, Simon M., Research and Development Reports 1, 4, 9, 12 and 16, U.S. Patent Office. Available from Publications Office, Dept. of Commerce.

6. Luhn, H.P., "Statistical Approach to Mechanized Encoding and Searching of Literary Information," I.B.M. Journal of Research and Development, 1, No. 4 (Oct., 1957).

Chapter II

Theory of Indexing Methods

This Chapter deals with the "connections" between index terms. The oldest form of connection was the hierarchical relationship. The newer form of connection is "coordination," "intersection," or "conjunction."

History and Analysis of the Information Control Problem

The origin of the classification concept

Until a few centuries ago the totality of recorded knowledge was small. Few books were written and each could be classified in one or more of the few then recognized sciences and fields of human endeavor.

The 18th century brought about a great increase in knowledge of the physical world, most of which was taxonomic in nature. This knowledge lent itself to classification. Cataloging and classifying became one of the important goals of science and classification system gained enormous importance. The hope that all knowledge necessary for the understanding of the physical world would soon be complete and fit into a "natural" and "universal" classification system became one of the fondest dreams of the age.

The importance of classification systems was based on the urge to see order in knowledge and to organize all knowledge into a closed system. Although subsequent developments relegated classification systems to a far less important position, vestiges of the enormous prestige gained at that time persist today.

The breakdown of classification in the era of technology

The Industrial Revolution created a new body of knowledge that was different in nature and much larger than all preceding knowledge. Moreover, the center shifted from the natural sciences to technology and its supporting sciences; to the knowledge of how to build railroads, ships, airplanes and power plants; how to cultivate the soil, cure diseases, etc. Not only did the nature and size of our store of knowledge change radically, but the need to consult the store of information increased.

This technological information created a new problem of information storage and retrieval. When information is scattered through a great many different articles and reports and when each of these "items of information" contains bits of intelligence related to or of potential importance to a number of different subjects a new order of information control arises. It is this diffuseness of technological information which causes and defines the information control problem as it faces us today.

Diffuseness of information implies that items of information may be of interest for a great many problems, applications and fields of pure and applied science. It implies that these items should be indexed

from each view-point of potential importance. The diffuseness of an item of information, therefore, is measured by its number of potential indexing viewpoints or
criteria. The high degree of diffuseness of technological
information is not accidental. It is inherent in the
nature of our technological civilization that every dis-
covery or achievement in one particular field may be
of interest in almost any other field.

The degree of diffuseness of information is the
heart of the indexing problem and the main factor in a
generalized theory of indexing. If an information collection is assembled for very special purposes only,
its indexing will cover only a fraction of all the potential uses of the information. When the index is to encompass the all potential applications, indexing depth
must cover all foreseeable implications.

The Problem of Class Inclusion

To understand the reason for the breakdown of
classification systems in their application to technological information, it is necessary to analyze briefly the
problem of "class-inclusion" or, more generally, the
problem of subordination. Although most apparent in
classification systems, the problem of subordination
is basic to any form of indexing.

The simplest form of analysis is that of indexing
according to only one particular criterion or from one
particular point of view. In such cases it is frequently possible to set up mutually exlusive classes. Even
when no fully mutually exclusive classes are possible,

the degree of overlap of these various classes will, in general, be small. In the Patent Office, where the main problem has centered around structural differences and similarities, it has been possible to maintain a classification according to mechanical structure. This has not been accomplished without very serious problems. Even the analysis of mechanical structure is subject to differences of point of view. Mutually exclusive classes exist to a limited degree only.

On the other hand, most of our present information collections consist of highly diffuse information which requires indexing from many viewpoints, such as design components, design principles, possible uses and applications, materials used, physical principles involved, sciences involved, production methods involved, etc. Each viewpoint requires an entirely different order of subordination. Technological documents may be indexed from a practically unlimited number of index critera or viewpoints. Some of the criteria may seem trivial, but even the most specialized viewpoints often represent major industries to which such parochial viewpoints are vital. As the technological evolution progresses, fresh viewpoints constantly emerge, and older viewpoints decrease in importance.

It is maintained by some that although many varying "special" indexing viewpoints of secondary importance do exist, there must be one "absolute" or general indexing criterion which can serve every purpose equally well. "Structure" has been quoted as an ex-

ample of such an absolute criterion, but the recent
shift or emphasis in physics has shown the relativity
rather than absoluteness of this Newtonian viewpoint.
There are also, in many fields of activity, special indexing criteria which seem of preponderant importance,
mostly because they were historically the first to
emerge and the prevalent nomenclature is still based
on them. However, no one has yet demonstrated any
absolute criteria or absolute classifications for the
purposes of the technological sciences, which present
an ever-widening and changing spectrum of indexing
criteria.

Various types of classification systems

The implications of a high degree of diffuseness of
information can be illustrated by a very simple classification problem: living beings can be indexed or classified acoording to a large number of criteria, for example: (a) skeletal structure, (b) reproductive system,
(c) circulatory system, (d) digestive system, (e) skin
structure, (f) habitat, (g) usefulness to human society.
Each criterion or "viewpoint" can form the basis of a
"classification." Figs. 5 and 6 show schematically a
classification based on criterion a or criterion b. This
form of classification can be termed "single-criterion
classification." The classes A_1, A_2, A_3, etc. or the
sub-classes A_{11}, A_{12}, A_{13}, etc. could, of course, be
arranged alphabetically. However, a more meaningful
order of the indexing criterion is usually attempted.
This order may be based on a size relationship or a

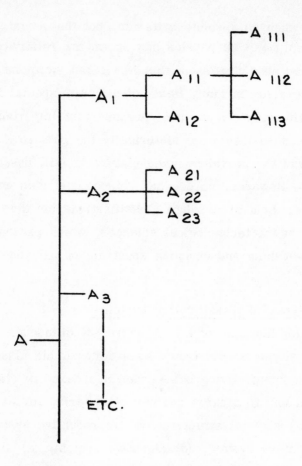

Figure 5. "Single Criterion Classification." Classifica-
Based on Indexing Criterion a, Skeleton
Structure.

56

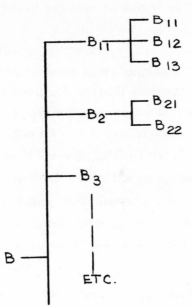

Figure 6. "Single Criterion Classification." Classification Based on Indexing Criterion b, Reproductive System.

relationship of time or space, on some causal relationship or on a combination of relationships. In drawing up a classification of internal combustion engines upon the criterion of structure we can start at the input side of the engine and enumerate all the parts as they contribute and relate to the power generating process. We would, in that case, start with the carburetor, and go through the valves into the cylinders; from there on through the pistons, connecting rods, etc., to the power output shaft. This would be a subordination based on a causal principle. A combination of causal and spacial relationships would be required to cover all parts of an engine completely.

Each of the seven single-criterion classifications of living beings in the example given above is incompatible with and different from the others. Each of these can serve only one field of interest or one type of user. A universal classification of interest to all possible users would, therefore, have to integrate all these points of view through indexing by all seven criteria. Figure 7 shows schematically a classification based on a combination of only two different indexing criteria. The larger the number of indexing criteria, the more complicated such a classification becomes. Although in practice only a small part of all possible combinations will actually be used, the classification system attempts to provide sufficient classes for all anticipated needs. The task is staggering, and that of keeping it up to date to provide new or changed criteria is still more staggering. The cost is prohibitive. It is rare that more than two indexing criteria are used.

The main problem in drawing up a classification system is that of making the decision as to which criterion should constitute the main class and which criteria should constitute the sub-classes and sub-sub-classes.

If, in the above example, it were decided to use criterion a, "skeleton structure" to draw up the main classes, and criteria b, "reproductive system" and c, "circulatory system," etc. for the sub-classes and sub-sub-classes respectively, this classification would be

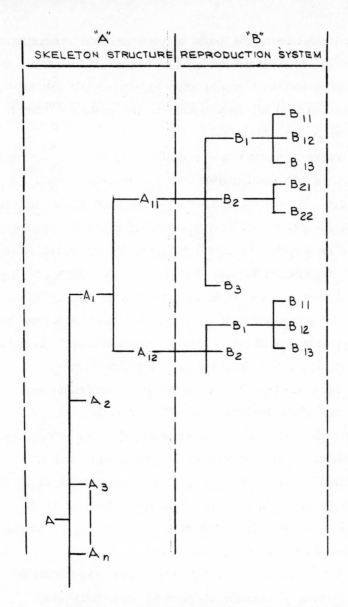

Figure 7. "Unpermuted Multiple Criterion Classification." Classification Based on Criterion "A" as Main Criterion and Criterion "B" as Sub-Criterion.

most useful from the point of view of bone specialists. However, a user interested in criterion g, "usefulness to human society," would have to consult all sub-sub-classes to find all information in the system of potential interest to him.

Where a narrow and specific purpose is concerned, this form of classification can prove quite useful. A research laboratory interested in data on stress failures of engine parts will find it useful to classify engines based on engine structural components and parts as the main indexing criterion, with the various forms of load and stresses responsible for failures as sub-criteria.

The above form of classification may be termed an "unpermuted multiple-criterion classification." In such unpermuted classifications each item of information need be classified in one way only. No cross-reference structure is required. If an article contains more than one item of information, for instance, information on heat stress in turbine wheels and on torsional vibration stress in crankshafts, each of these items of information will, of course, have to be indexed separately from the other. However, no cross-reference structure is called for.

The unpermuted multiple-criterion classification is the form of classification most frequently used. It is generally considered to be the "purest" form of classification. For the purposes of the generalized theory it will be considered the definition and general model of a classification.

The alphabetic subject heading list

Unpermuted multiple-criterion classifications can meet only special purposes, those in which the subordination of indexing criteria lends itself to the requirements of the special purpose, as in the example of engine failure data. A "universal" information retrieval system to meet all possible requirements would, therefore, have to consist of a larger number of different classifications, each with a different hierarchical subordination or "permutation" of the indexing criteria.

Instead of keeping the different classifications separate, it would appear potentially more economical to integrate or merge them into one "universal" system. But when attempts are made to effect such a merger, it is found that there are no relationships between the classes (other than that of their symbols) upon which their order can be based. In other words, there is no practical alternative to merging the main classes A_1, A_2, A_3.........and B_1, B_2, B_3....... of all these classifications alphabetically according to the first letter of main classes. In doing this the concept of meaningful hierarchical relationships is abandoned. Even small amounts of permutation force this abandonment, and permuted classifications cannot, therefore, be considered "true" classifications.

Actually, such a fully permuted classification would be identical with a fully permuted alphabetic subject heading list. That a classification scheme and an alphabetic subject heading list are basically identical, is a remarkable conclusion.

In practice any permuted classification cannot be complete and is extremely fragmentary at best. Permuting a classification requires that each item of information be classified in as many ways as the number of permutations of the indexing criteria on which the classification is based. It also requires a corresponding cross-reference structure. Thus an alphabetic subject heading list will always be fragmentary, an incomplete form of a permuted multiple-criterion classification.

Suming up, it can be said that classification systems have been found practical only under two conditions: (a) where there is an unambiguous and unchanging subordination of the indexing criteria as well as of the retrieval criteria; (b) where the indexing criteria are fixed and very limited in number. In other words, hierarchical classifications are practical only where information of a low degree of diffuseness is concerned and the system is intended only for a particular use.

The difficulties encountered in classification schemes have intensified as the degree of diffuseness of the information has increased. As a result, libraries have tended more and more toward alphabetic subject heading systems. This transition was a gradual process leading to a continuing replacement of hierarchical classification by alphabetical subject heading systems. Many existing classifications actually are

mixed forms which show many characteristics of the
subject heading list. The alphabetic subject heading
list relieves the system of the embarrassing necessity
to decide which criteria to subordinate to other criteria. It provides a less bulky and less expensive apparatus that is easier to maintain and has sufficient
flexibility to permit incorporation of new indexing criteria.

The advent of correlative indexes

With the emergence of special libraries serving
industry and government and with the related development of technical information and research data centers,
alphabetic subject headings were in turn challenged by
Descriptors[1] and Uniterms[2] and various other closely
related systems of "key word indexing."

This introduced a relationship that differs radically
from the hierarchical form. This relationship is
coincidence, coordination, collation or correlation between or among terms. This type of indexing developed
along with mechanized searching devices.

The advantages and disadvantages of the various
systems of what is generally referred to as "key word
indexing" are well-known. Moreover these indexing
systems have been expanded, and elaborated to encompass functions, hierarchical relationships and syntactical problems. They are based on key words taken
from or suggested by the text or on key-concepts rather
than single words. The concept may be a two-or three-
word term, a descriptive phrase, or a subject heading.

The generic name for this type of indexing is "concept coordination," which is based on the search instead of the indexing. Each of the many systems of key word indexing has its own advantages, disadvantages and areas of application.

In the original form of Uniterm indexing, key words were taken from or suggested by the text and used as index terms, without consulting The Vocabulary of Index Terms. Under this theory, after the collection reached a certain size, the vocabulary should automatically stabilize. A cross-reference structure must be provided to take care of synonyms, etc. In its simplest form key-word indexing provides the greatest possible quantitative retrieval power because any single term or any combination of index terms can be used to retrieve an item of information.

If properly indexed, an item of information is indexed by any key word that is or could possibly become of importance to any potential user of the item of information. Therefore, it is also, in theory, automatically indexed by any or all possible combinations of these terms. The combinations normally include all subject headings or classes and sub-classes by which this item of information would have been indexed had a subject heading list or a classification system been used, and some others which may or may not be pertinent.

These advantages are, however, bought at a price. This price is the acceptance of a rudimentary "access apparatus," usually consisting of no more than an alphabetic listing of the complete vocabulary of index terms in use in the system. Such a listing cannot directly tell the user what information is contained in the system. For example, a vocabulary of index terms listing the term "water" as well as the term "pump" does not necessarily imply that the system contains any information on water pumps, nor does the presence of the term "jet" as well as the term "engine" necessarily imply the presence of information on jet engines. In other words, there is no way of ascertaining a priori whether the combined terms "water pump" and "jet engines" are "true" or "false" combinations until the search process is completed and the documents are consulted.

Another characteristic of Uniterm Indexing is the absence of hierarchical definition within each indexing criterion. Indexing tends to be performed at the level at which the concept happens first to be referred to in the text. For instance, an Army general indexed by the criterion of military rank is simply indexed by the term "generals" instead of "field officers," or "officers" or "soldiers" or any combination of these. A search for everything on "soldiers" may, therefore, require searches by each of the above terms. For these purposes a cross-reference structure has to be maintained in the access apparatus. An exhaustive search by a combination of terms may require a number of individual searches by various combinations of various terms. Therefore, the low indexing cost is obtained at the price of a higher search cost.

It is possible to alleviate the lack of suggestiveness of the vocabulary, noted above, by using longer index terms. Instead of the elementary terms "pump," "water," "jet," and "engine," combined terms like "water pump" and "jet engine" can be used. Such a vocabulary of index terms will become suggestive of the contents of the information system and fewer individual searches will be required to obtain full search results, but it also comes closer to the conventional subject heading list.

Lengthening the average index term produces changes in two other characteristics. The first change is a reduction of retrieval power. In using the combined terms "water pump" and "jet engine," we can no longer retrieve complete information by the broader terms "pumps" or "engines." Also if the item of information dealt with water jets but was not indexed by this term the possibility of retrieving by the term water jets at a later time is lost. Automatically indexing by every occurrence of the elementary terms "water," "pump," "jet" and "engine" would have preserved this possibility of retrieval of all references to water jets.

The other change accompanying a lengthening of the index terms is a reduction in the false combinations of terms, and the possibility of non-pertinent combinations, such as "water engine" and "jet pump" disappears.

If this process of lengthening of the index terms is continued, the combination of terms may eventually become conventional subject headings.

Thus while in the current practice of information retrieval there appears to be a great and basic gulf between hierarchical systems and concept coordination, in theory one is only a special case of the other.

Most indexing systems are based on a combination of two forms of connectedness between terms: the hierarchical connection and the "coordinative" (or "intersective") connection.

The proof is in the present use of practically any type of subject heading list. Each of the headings is hierarchical in nature. For example, headings such as "engine, pump" or "engine, pump, water" have hierarchical relationships among their terms. However, each document is usually indexed by three to ten different subject headings. The relationships among these headings is coordinative.

It is true that in a printed and bound index we cannot perform retrieval by coordination except by a manual sorting process. However, the relationship between the headings is coordinative and once the same index information is entered into a machine system, coordinative searches can easily be performed.

General Theory of Indexing Methods
The "Connective Continuum"

The preceding sections have traced the history and evolution of information retrieval problems. This evolution has been a gradual process during which one system automatically developed into another, and the various known indexing systems appear to form a continuum rather than contrasting systems.

This continuum is schematically illustrated in Figs. 8a, b and c. The factor that determines position in the continuum is the average length of index terms, measured as the average number of words per term. Since we have defined the word "term" as either a single word or a hierarchical chain such as a subject heading, the average number of words per term is actually directly proportional to the degree of hierarchical connectedness and is inversely proportional to the degree of coordinative connectedness.

Thus the curve for the average length of term, becomes a straight line (Fig. 8c). The curve for the degree of hierarchical definition will be identical (Fig. 8f). The curve for the need of a coordinating mechanism is, of course, the same as the curve for the degree of coordinative connectedness. It is the inverse of the curve of Figs. 8c and 8f and is shown in Fig. 8i.

Fig. 8b shows the relative positions of the various methods of indexing in the continuum. Depending on the width or narrowness with which we define each of these systems, the areas covered by their designations either overlap to some extent or leave a certain amount of gap. However, no matter how we define these areas, the entire spectrum is actually used in practice.

One end of the continuum represents indexing exclusively by the smallest single words available. That is, it uses the smallest "units" available. Such a system will, therefore, use the largest possible number of terms per item indexed. At this position in the continuum we would, for example, index an article on the "erosion of turbine buckets in bunker-C oil burning jet engines" by the single terms "erosion," "turbine," "bucket," "bunker-C," "oil," "jet" and "engines." This is the area of keyword indexing in its purest form.

"Coordinative"	"Hierarchical"
or	or
"Short Term End"	"Long Term End"
of Continuum	of Continuum

Fig. 8 (a)

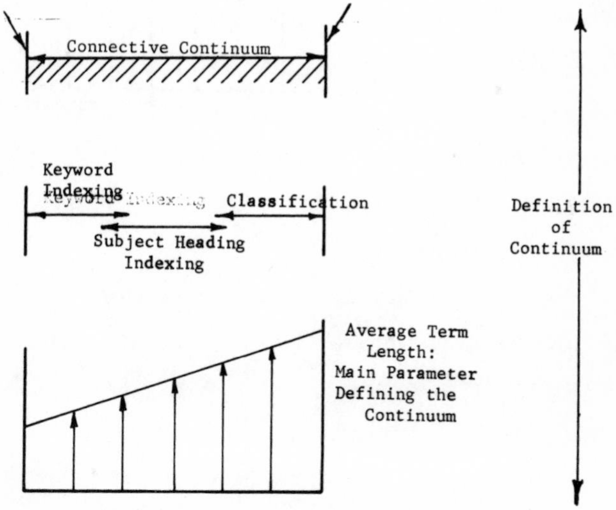

Fig. 8 (b)

Fig. 8 (c)

69

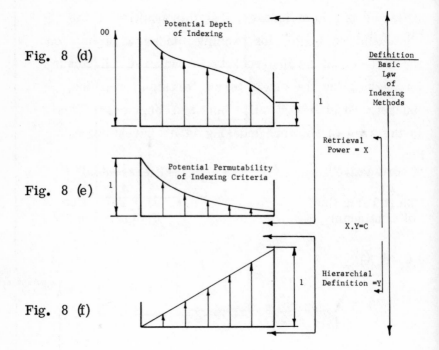

Fig. 8 (d)

Fig. 8 (e)

Fig. 8 (f)

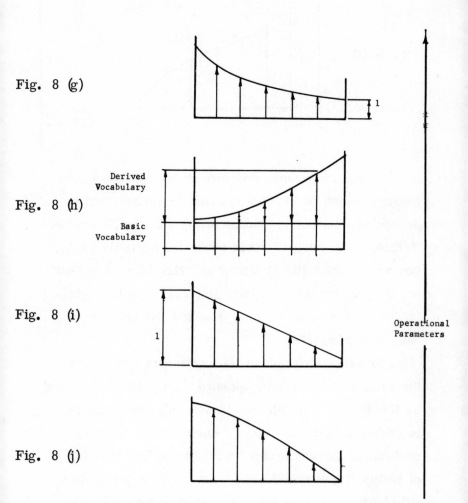

Fig. 8 (g)

1

Fig. 8 (h)

Derived
Vocabulary

Basic
Vocabulary

Fig. 8 (i)

1

Fig. 8 (j)

Operational
Parameters

Fig. 8 (k)

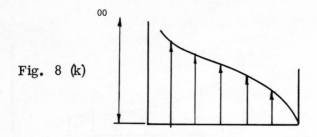

Moving away from this end of the continuum, the average length of the index terms increases. In the preceding example individual terms like "jet," "engine," "turbine" and "bucket" would gradually be replaced by combined terms like "engine, jet" and "turbine bucket" or "turbine, bucket"; "engine, jet; and "erosion engines, jet." At this point we have reached the area of the subject heading list.

The other extreme of the continuum represents the area of hierarchical classification. Here we index by the longest possible terms and only one term is required to index an item of information. At this position in the continuum an article on the "erosion of turbine"blades" in bunker-C oil burning jet engines" would be indexed by classes, sub-classes, sub-sub-classes, etc., for example as follows: "internal combustion engines, steady-state engines, gas turbines, turbine blades; liquid fuel, mineral fuel, bunker-C oil; wear, erosion." For the purposes of this general theory the above classification will be considered one

72

single indexing "term" since it designates only one particular place in the classification.

It should be noted that the above classification is an unpermuted multiple-criterion classification having structure as its main criterion, fuels as sub-criterion, and operational troubles as a sub-sub criterion. In practice most classifications will not have more than two indexing criteria, so that the possibility of indexing by additional criteria, such as operational troubles is commonly lost at this end of the continuum.

Basic Law of Indexing Methods

In addition to the main or defining parameter, the average term length, the continuum possesses a number of "derived" parameters which are functions of the main parameter.

The most important derived parameter is the potential depth of indexing. This parameter, which is proportional to the number of potential index criteria per item that can be used, is shown schematically in Fig. 8d. For a pure classification system this value is unity since one cannot index by a larger number of indexing criteria than those that have specifically been built into the classification. As we move away in the continuum and shed the constraints of classification systems discussed in earlier sections, larger numbers of indexing criteria can be utilized without undue penalties in cost and complexity. When we reach the other extreme in the continuum, almost unlimited indexing depth becomes feasible.

73

This indicates that, in general, the more diffuse the information, the more important it becomes to stay at the short-term end of the continuum.

Indexing depth, however, involves more than just the number of indexing terms that can be combined for a search. Permutability of retrieval criteria, schematically shown in Fig. 8e, is an important related criterion. In a classification for retrieval by one indexing criterion only, this must be the criterion on which the main classes are based. For retrieval by two criteria, these must be the criteria on which the main classes and first sub-classes respectively have been based, etc. We cannot retrieve by a single criterion which forms only the sub-classes or the sub-sub-classes. At this end of the spectrum permutability is, therefore, equal to zero. On moving toward the other end of the spectrum, more and more permutability of retrieval criteria is obtained until at the short-term end of the continuum complete permutability is available.

The two parameters discussed above provide a yardstick of the accuracy with which information can be indexed and the detail in which information can be retrieved. These are therefore combined in the term retrieval power. This is the most important single feature of an indexing system.

The degree of hierarchical definition has been discussed earlier (Fig. 8f). In a classification system there is a 100 percent hierarchical definition, since to index by any one criterion is to index by all possible hierarchical levels. In our previous example of an item of information on the "erosion of turbine blades in bunker-C grade oil burning jet engines," each of the three possible indexing criteria, "structure" or "fuel" or "operational troubles" was indexed by all possible hierarchical levels: the structure as "turbine blades, turbines, steady-state engines, internal combustion engines;" the fuel as "bunker-C grade oil, mineral fuel, liquid fuel." Operation troubles could have been indexed as "erosion, wear," if the classification had provided for the possibility of a third indexing criterion.

At the other end of the continuum, the area of keyword indexing, hierarchical definition disappears from the retrieval apparatus. Using our previous example again, and indexing this document by "structure," whether we index simply by the term "turbine blades" or by the next higher level, such as "gas turbines," or by a still higher level or any combination of these, becomes more or less arbitrary.

In selecting index terms there are only two degrees of freedom, namely the index criterion we use and the hierarchical level within this criterion. The first degree of freedom corresponds to the combination retrieval power shown in Figs. 8d and 8e. The second corresponds to the degree of hierarchical definition shown in Fig. 8f Although no exact mathematical treatment is as yet available, it seems clear that greater hierarchical definition can be obtained only at the expense of retrieval power and visa versa. If X designates the "retrieval power" and Y designates the hierarchical definition, this relationship could be roughly expressed as follows: $X \cdot Y^2 = $ Constant.

When a search has to be performed in a system located at the short-term end of the continuum where the hierarchical definition is low, a complete search may involve a number of individual searches using terms of different hierarchical level. In a search by two terms of different indexing criteria, each having a number of possible hierarchical levels, it is necessary to search by each of all possible permutations. In contrast with this, at the other extreme of the continuum, the area of pure classification, only one search is required. The number of individual searches required for a complete systems search is schematically shown as a parameter in Fig. 8g.

Another parameter of importance to the economics of the system is the size of the access apparatus. This is indicated in Fig. 8h. At the short-term end of the continuum the access apparatus consists merely in the alphabetic list of the smallest single words used for indexing. This basic vocabulary is usually relatively small.

At the long-term end of the continuum the access apparatus includes combinations of these single words. The number of these combinations increases greatly as the combinations get longer and longer.

Fig. 8i shows the need for a mechanical coordination or coincidence mechanism as a function of the

main parameter, average term length. As indicated
earlier, this will be a straight line. At the short-
term end of the continuum a coordinating mechanism
is indispensable. At the other extreme no such mechanism is required. In the middle of the continuum
there may be a need to search for the coincidence of
subject headings. Without a coordinating mechanism
the potential depth of indexing and retrieval shown at
the short-term end in Fig. 8d remains a potential only.
The same conclusion holds for all other parameters.
The actual values of the parameters which are obtained will otherwise be far less favorable.

Fig. 8j shows the possibility of false coordinations
of two or more terms as a function of the average
term length. As explained in the previous section, it
is zero at the long-term end of the continuum and a
maximum at the short-term end. False coordinations
do not result in loss of information, but in the retrieval of some non-pertinent documents among all the
required pertinent documents. It is a "noise" factor.

Fig. 8k shows the capacity for handling semantic
indeterminacy, that is, the capacity of an indexing
system for indexing in areas where a sharply defined
and well-standardized vocabulary is not yet available.
As explained previously, classifications cannot handle
this type of "frontier" information very well. The
closer the position to the short-term end of the spectrum, the greater the capacity to handle semantic
ambiguities or indeterminacy. At the extreme short-

term end it increases to an almost infinite degree, and even the vaguest concepts can be described by putting a number of different terms together to form a kind of telegraphic description of the concept. Any one or any combination of these terms can then be used to retrieve the information item.

The general theory of indexing as presented above should be open to mathematical treatment. The parameters presented so far are mathematical in nature. The curves shown are, of course, only schematic indications of the true mathematical functions. Determination of their exact shapes will have to await more objective establishment of the mathematical relationships.

Cost Parameters

In addition to these operational parameters a number of others could be listed. These would be cost parameters. Although the full mathematical development would be quite complex, certain general conclusions seem possible. These are:

1. That the cost of indexing input is lowest on the short-term end of the spectrum and highest on the long-term end.

2. That the searching cost, (output cost) will be low for hierarchical searches. A pure hierarchical classification should allow immediate retrieval by a single search. This makes for low search cost. On the short-term end of the continuum every search

question may involve a number of individual searches. Higher search costs can, therefore, be expected at the short-term end of the continuum.

We want to emphasize that all of these curves represent tendencies only. The straight lines are the only accurate representations since they are based on definitions.

Venn-diagram Representation of the Continuum

As we have seen, at the right side of the continuum only hierarchical relationships exist; in the middle, a combination of hierarchical relationships and co-ordination exist; and at the left we approach the area where only concept coordination is used.

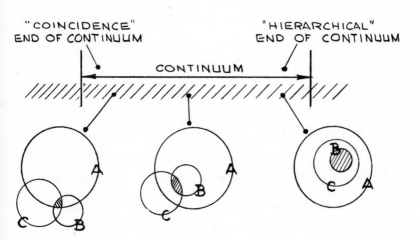

Fig. 9

This is illustrated in Fig. 9 for the case of a document indexed by three terms. At the left side of the continuum it is indexed as A; B; C. In the middle of A, B; C and at the right as A, B, C.

Selection of Position in the Continuum

When we have information of low diffuseness, which does not require more than one or two different indexing criteria, and when these criteria always have the same hierarchical subordination, we can, in theory, operate at any point on the continuum and use either classification or key word indexing.

For information of high diffuseness for which permutability of the indexing criteria is required, we have no choice but to operate at the short-term end of the continuum regardless of the ratio of input to output load, as it is only at the short-term end that full permutability and the highest possible indexing depth is available.

References

1. Mooers, Calvin N., "Scientific Information Retrieval Systems for Machine Operation -- Case Studies in Design," Zator Technical Bulletin 66 (1951), Zator Co., 140 1/2 Mt. Auburn St., Boston, Mass.

2. Sanford, J. A., and Theriault, F. R., "Problems in the Application of Uniterm Coordinate Indexing," College and Research Libraries, 17, No. 1:19-23 (Jan., 1956).

Chapter III Integration of Continua

Connection Between "Terminological Continuum"
And
"Connective Continuum"

The terminological continuum deals with terms regardless of their relationships.

The connective continuum deals with the connections between terms, which could be based either on hierarchical subordination or on coincidence or a combination of both. The connective mode of retrieval reaches its maximum and becomes unity (all connective) at the short-term end of the continuum (the area of key word indexing) and approaches zero at the long-term end (the area of the pure classification system). The second mode of retrieval, retrieval by hierarchical subordination, reaches a maximum value (all hierarchical) at the extreme long-term end and approaches zero at the short-term end. The middle of the continuum is the area corresponding roughly to most subject-heading systems.

In practice the design an I.R. system requires selection of a place in each of the two continua. The place of an I.R. system in the terminological continuum is determined by the level of terminology used-- lay language or professional terminology or a mixture of these.

81

If, for example, the use of a fully professional language has been decided upon for indexing electronic literature, every term of this terminology should be treated as one word and be indivisible from the viewpoint of the logic of the system. For example, an item of index information like "oscillator-circuit; frequency modulation; 100 megacycles; carrier-wave" comprises four different professional terms. Each of these should be considered indivisible.

After the level of terminology has been decided upon a determination has to be made as to what system of indexing will be used.

If no hierarchical relationships of any kind are recognized among these four terms, the I.R. system operates at the short-term end of the connective continuum, the keyword area, and retrieval is performed by search for coincidence of terms.

If certain hierarchical relations among these terms are recognized, then the I.R. system operates in the middle of the descriptive continuum. This would be the case when the I.R. system features subject headings like "oscillator circuit, frequency modulation" and "carrier-wave, 100 megacycles."

When hierarchical relationships exist among all four of these terms, the I.R. system operates as a pure classification system. Such a system would have hierarchical ladders such as "oscillator-circuit, carrier-wave, frequency-modulation, 100 megacycles."

Because each I.R. system is described by a

point on the continua, it would also be represented as one point in a two-dimensional plane. This is shown in Fig. 10. The heaviness of shading indicates the most heavily used areas. The lighter shaded areas are used in special cases only. Thus, the proposed Patent Office structural language, when designed for use with a mechanized retrieval device, would be represented by Point A. When designed to operate as a classification scheme it would be represented by Point B.

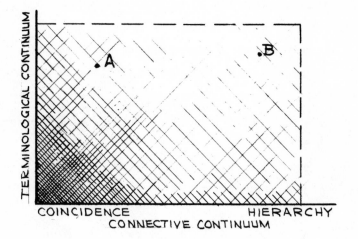

Fig. 10

Chapter IV Basic Principles of Information Retrieval Devices

The Nature of a Theory of I. R. Devices[1]

Every well-developed machine art features certain basic considerations to guide the designer in laying out his machine design, and the user in planning his applications. In developing his design, the designer proceeds from the most fundamental considerations available to him to considerations which are usually of a less abstract nature, and from there on to the design details. The potential user should follow the same path in analyzing machine systems.

These primary considerations of an abstract nature will be discussed at some length; the secondary considerations concern the nature of choice of memory elements and coding system and will be treated only briefly. The primary considerations will be used as a framework for classifying the various types of information retrieval systems. This theory, therefore, presents basically a classification of I.R. devices.

As is now well known in the I.R. art, there is no such a thing as a "unique" classification. Depending on the viewpoint and interest of the user, numerous quite different and incompatible approaches to classifying a body of information are possible.

The form of classification presented here is based

on the requirements of the I.R. field as we see them. It intends to classify I.R. devices as those that will or will not meet the fundamental requirements of the I.R. field. This form of classification is no more than a practical frame of reference to allow us to see similarities and differences and to apply some systematic thinking to the problems of information retrieval machines. It may help create some order out of the ever-growing chaos of claims of competing systems.

Limitation of Present Treatment of the Problem

A. The oldest forms of information retrieval systems utilize memories based on cards, tapes, sheets of paper, or other suitable materials. In general, scanning of these records involves some form of physical movement of records over a reading head or the movement of reading heads over records. This form of memory will be referred to as movable memories. In contrast to this, electronic memories which are stationary, and which involve only electric currents and changes of state of the memory elements, are developing. This form of memory will be referred to as stationary memories.

Although the same form of analysis applies to systems based on either type of memories, the advantages and disadvantages of the various basic principles frequently vary greatly for each of these two types of memories. Each of these types of devices should, therefore, be treated separately. This discussion is limited to systems based on movable memories. "Stationary memories" are not yet of practical importance for I.R. purposes.

B. In analyzing the fundamentals of I.R. devices, no distinction will be made between devices which carry only the search data and devices which carry the full document as well.

In current practice of mechanized I.R. the "document store" (the "file") and the "retrieval device" (the "index") are generally separated. I.R. devices will, therefore, be treated as search devices which yield a series of addresses as the end result of a search. These addresses usually take the form of serial numbers which are used to locate the documents themselves. The provision of the documents may be done manually, semi-automatically or fully automatically.

From the point of view of the current, mechanized, I.R. art, document storage and retrieval is generally considered a minor problem, and is overshadowed by problems of searching.

Definition of Information Retrieval Machines

Most machines are in principle only labor-saving devices made to facilitate previously manual processes. Such machines differ only in the degree to which they mechanize a process. They can provide an almost infinite variety of mechanization ranging from the simplest aids to the most complicated fully automatic machines.

There may be some types of machines and devices that achieve end results which could not be achieved without them, but present-day information retrieval machines are apparently not of this nature. They do not create any new capabilities but only mechanize certain previously manual functions.

Keeping in mind the fact that I.R. machines are strictly labor-saving devices, we may now consider the following two questions:

1. What are the information retrieval functions that are most in need of mechanization?

2. Is there a point in the mechanization process at which an information retrieval system will be sufficiently mechanized to be considered a "machine system?"

Search for coincidence of terms (a coordination) can be performed manually by scanning documents, but this is not practical for large collections of literature. A search for coincidence of terms can, therefore, not really be considered practical for large collections unless the system features some form of coincidence device; usually a mechanical or electrical device or machine. On the other hand, searches by hierarchical subordination of concepts can, in principle, be performed without the help of mechanical devices.

It follows, therefore, that the inclusion of a device to determine coincidence of terms makes a system a "machine system." The "Uniterm" system[2] represents a borderline case. It is a manual system especially designed to facilitate the performance of term-coincidence searches and may be considered a "simulated machine system." By comparison, even the simplest form of edge notched card system[3] would be a true machine system. There are a great many possible coincidence mechanisms based on mechanical, electrical, optical, chemical and other principles. Coincidence mechanisms can easily be recognized in edge-notched card systems, field-punched card systems, magnetic tape systems, electronic memories, and others.

The "term-coincidence" function is the heart of every machine system. In principle, even the most complex search functions can be performed by means of a simple coincidence device.

Besides this "term-coincidence" function, there are many other functions that can be mechanized, such as recognition of terms or recognition of item numbers. In the simpler information storage and retrieval devices, these functions are frequently performed by a human operator. In the more complex systems other automatic functions, such as, coding, printout, etc., may be built into information retrieval machines.

The economics of mechanization of other functions in an I.R. device depend upon the nature of the device and will differ greatly from case to case. For example, in some cases it may be easy to store the complete document with the index data. In other cases the cost of doing this is prohibitive.

Primary Design Considerations

A. Store Organization or "Grouping"

In setting up an information retrieval system, we first index the items of information forming the information collection by assigning a number of "index terms" to each item of information. The next step involves entry of these index terms, the "index data," into the memory of the retrieval machine. In many cases a code is used for transforming the index data into storable units ("bits") in the machine's memory.

Generally, each item of information is given a serial number. The totality of index data can then be represented as in Figure 11, in which each item of

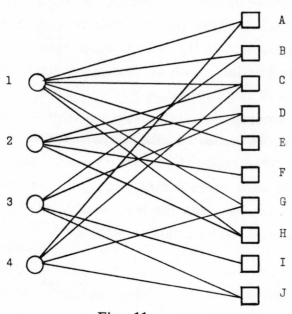

Fig. 11

information is connected to a number of terms, and
each term is connected to a number of items. In this
schematic representation, item 1 has been indexed by
terms A, B, C, E, G and H, item 2 has been indexed
by terms C, D, F and H, etc. Basically the index
information consists of the totality of "connections" between the items and the terms. Some of these connections, arbitrarily selected from Fig. 11, are shown
in Fig. 12.

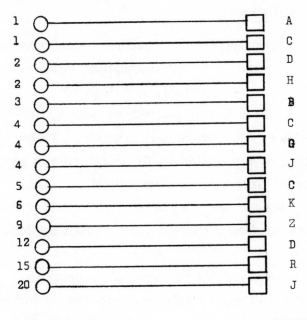

"ITEMS" OF INFORMATION   "TERMS"

Fig. 12

These connections can be coded and recorded, for
example, with one punched card for every connection. [4]
In that case both the item number and the term would

91

be punched on this card. But before these punched cards can be used for retrieval purposes, some form of "grouping" or sorting is desirable.

Although in principle a memory could be arranged as shown in Fig. 12 and searched for coincidence of terms, "grouping" may greatly reduce the size of the memory and simplify the search mechanism. Grouping makes it possible to reduce the redundant repetition of codes, as will become apparent below.

Conventional Grouping

Information retrieval is concerned with only two entities, namely, "items of information" (further referred to simply as "items"), and "terms." As a result, there are only two possible ways of grouping. Fig. 13 shows the conventional grouping. This form of grouping by single items will be referred to as Conventional Grouping, or Item Grouping. One example of such grouping would be a collection of the previously mentioned punched cards sorted by item (Fig. 14).

Another example of this type of grouping is a punched card or edge notched card system in which one card is dedicated to each item, and all of the terms by which an item has been indexed are coded on its card (Fig. 15). An important advantage is gained by grouping in this manner. Only half the original number of term codes and item codes will need to be entered into the system. By dedicating a card to

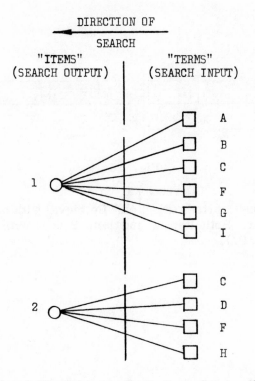

Conventional Grouping or Item Grouping: "Terms Arranged by "Item"

Fig. 13

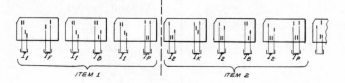

Fig. 14

Conventional Grouping

"Connections" sorted out. "Item" Retrieval with punched card sorter. Both Item 1 and Item 2 deal with the subject (B. P.).

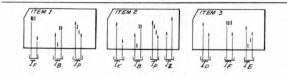

Fig. 15

Conventional Grouping

For retrieval with punched card scanners. Both Item 1 and Item 2 deal with the subject of (B. P.).

an item, the repetition of item codes can be eliminated. If a collection of i items, each indexed by n number of terms out of a total vocabulary of t terms is encoded without grouping, as shown in Fig. 12, a total of (2·n·i) codes are required.

Still another example of item grouping would be a magnetic tape[4] on which first all the terms of item 1 are entered together and next, all the terms of item 2, etc (Fig. 16). As these examples show, "grouping" is independent of the system of coding or form of record. It is even independent of whether a number of smaller records or one single large record is used.

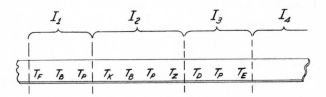

Fig. 16

Conventional Grouping

Magnetic Tape. Retrieval by linear scanning. Both items 1 and 2 deal with the subject of (B.P).

Conventional grouping is of particular importance for short-lived information. It generally allows more convenient entry of changes in information items, or removal of inactive information items than the alternative form of grouping.

This form of grouping is also particularly suited to accounting as it allows the complete item of information to be stored alongside the search information (frequently the two are merged). Thus information can be taken from the item and entered somewhere else while the scanning process is performed. In this manner payroll data, production data, etc. can be accumulated.

Practically all punched card systems, such as IBM, Remington Rand, Samas, Bull, as well as edge coded systems, such as McBee-Keysort, operate according to this grouping. Originally these systems were all designed for accounting purposes. Only because of the absence of systems based on more suitable principles have they been made to serve for literature searching.

Inverted Grouping

The second form of grouping, items grouped by single terms, is schematically shown in Fig. 17. It will be referred to as "Inverted Grouping," or "Term Grouping." It is the inverse of the conventional form of grouping. One example of this grouping is the Uniterm system of coordinate indexing in which each card is dedicated to a term and the serial numbers of items which have been indexed by that term are recorded in numeric characters in a special manner

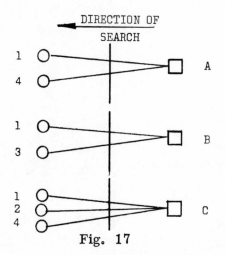

Fig. 17

Inverted Grouping or Term Grouping: "Items"
Arranged by "Terms"

on these cards (Fig. 18). The set of punched cards
mentioned earlier and shown in Fig. 14, this time
sorted by terms, is another example of inverted grouping (Fig. 19)[5]

Other examples are optical coincidence systems[6,10]
in which each card is dedicated to a term but in which
the serial numbers of the items which have been indexed by that term are punched at "dedicated positions" on the term card (Fig. 20).

Still another example would be a magnetic tape
system in which a portion of the tape is dedicated to

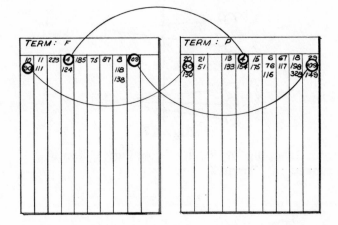

Fig. 18

Inverted Grouping

"Uniterm" system. Search based on visual comparison of numbers. A simulation of a Machine System. There are three documents, namely 4, 90 and 109 on the subject of terms (F. P).

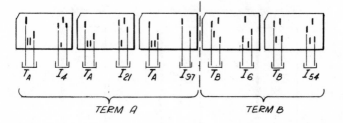

T_A I_4 T_A I_{2l} T_A I_{97} T_B I_6 T_B I_{54}

TERM A   TERM B

Fig. 19

Inverted Grouping
"Connections" sorted out by term.   Retrieval by means
of punched card collator.

TERM B				
SINGLE				
1	●	3	4	5
6	7	8	9	10
11	12	●	14	15
16	17	18	19	20
21	22	23	24	25
26	●	28	29	30

TERM K				
0-5 YRS. EXP.				
1	2	3	4	●
6	7	8	9	10
11	12	●	14	15
16	17	18	19	20
21	22	23	24	25
26	27	28	29	●

TERM P				
COLLEGE ED.				
1	2	3	4	5
6	7	8	9	10
11	12	●	14	15
16	17	18	19	20
21	22	23	24	25
26	27	28	●	30

Fig. 20

Inverted Grouping

Search based on superimposition of Termcards and
identification of serial number of the coinciding holes.
There is one item, namely 13, meeting the requirements of terms (B.K.P.) System known as superimposable card system peek-a-boo system or optical coincidence system.

99

a term, and the item codes are grouped under a particular term coded on the tape (Fig. 21).

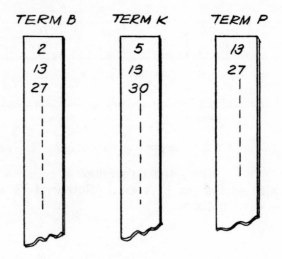

TERM B   TERM K   TERM P

2   5   13
13   13   27
27   30

Fig. 21

Inverted Grouping

A Magnetic Tape for every term. Search by scanning of tapes in computer and comparison of numbers.

Term grouping is generally better suited for I. R. purposes, but for smaller information collections of rapidly changing data, conventional grouping will give greater ease of entering changes and may have acceptably short search times.

After documents have been indexed, the index data appears in a form corresponding to conventional grouping. Organization according to inverted grouping frequently requires an extra step, the inversion. It will, therefore, frequently be cheapest and simplest to organize a collection in the conventional grouping.

There are only two systems in which the data can be entered directly in inverted grouping, at about the same data input cost as for conventional grouping. These are Uniterm systems and optical coincidence systems. The reason is that the data are entered on relatively small term cards which can be handled easily and rapidly. If term tapes are used, this sort of direct entry in inverted form is not practical and the inversion will have to be a separate step performed in a batch process.

Grouping permits the organization of the store of index data and the filing of records in an orderly manner. The next step is the searching of this store of index data.

B. Searching the Index Data ("Matching")

Grouping is easily recognizable as a major design consideration of information storage and retrieval systems. As the factor which governs the relation of "items" and "terms," it arises from the very definition of the information storage and retrieval problem.

The other parameters of design may be derived from examination of the retrieval action: Grouping was required to organize the index data into a form upon which a search can be performed. This search or "matching" operation consists of the comparison of the "search code," constituting a question, with the "memory codes." This action permits a degree of

101

Basic
Information Retrieval
Devices

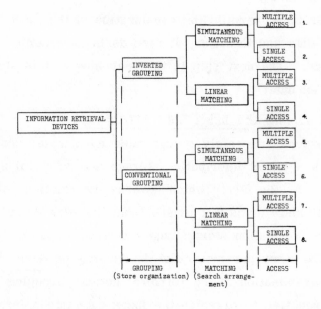

Fig. 22

freedom, namely, whether only one comparison can be made at a time or whether the search pattern can be compared to many or all memory patterns simultaneously. This constitutes the second basic parameter, "Matching."

There are two different ways of matching, namely, "Sequential Matching" and "Simultaneous Matching." In sequential matching the code patterns of the memory are compared one by one with the search pattern or patterns. In simultaneous matching, a very substantial part of, or all memory code patterns are simultaneously compared to a search pattern. The difference between these two forms of matching is really a matter of degree, and mixed systems, which are hard to fit in either of these two classes, are possible.

As shown in Fig. 22 the grouping and matching yield a total of four different systems. An example of conventional grouping and sequential or linear matching would be a punched card scanner (Fig. 23).

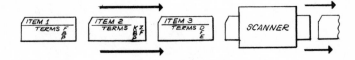

Fig. 23
Conventional Grouping
Sequential Matching

An example of conventional grouping and simultaneous matching could be visualized as a collection of cards, each dedicated to an item of information, each of these cards having their terms notched out along its edge. The selection device would feature "selection bars," running under the entire collection of cards and engaging the edge coding. Thus the entire collection could be interrogated simultaneously. A system of this nature could be visualized as a large Electrofile machine[7] with a very large number of selection bars (Fig. 24).

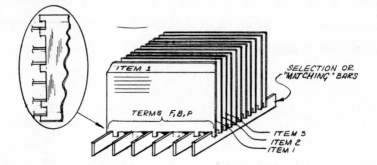

Fig. 24

Conventional Grouping
Simultaneous Matching

Superimposable card systems are an example of inverted grouping and simultaneous scanning. In these systems, large rectangular cards are dedicated to terms. Each item of information has a position dedicated to its serial number in such a manner that very large sections of information collections or entire collections can be searched simultaneously for coincidence of terms by superimposing a number of "term cards," and observing coincidence of holes. In doing this, all documents are simultaneously "matched" or "scanned" (Fig. 25).

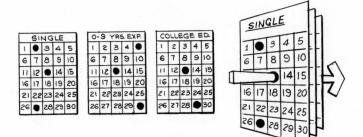

Fig. 25

Inverted Grouping
Simultaneous Matching

Optical Coincidence System

Inverted grouping and sequential matching yield collating systems. Collating systems may be based on a number of media. Best known are punched card collators but collators based on magnetic tapes, each dedicated to a term, are possible. It is, in principle, possible to build collators in which three or more terms may be collated simultaneously. However, all existing systems collate only two terms at a time. The result of this process is then collated against the third term, etc. (Fig. 26).

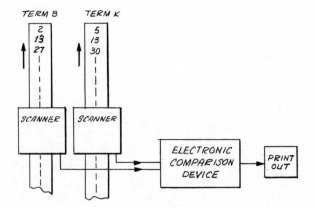

Fig. 26

Inverted Grouping
Sequential Matching

Simultaneous Matching provides rapid search. Inverted Grouping and Simultaneous Matching will, of course, give the fastest search. However, this higher search speed may in many cases be accompanied by the extra expense of an inversion step. This inversion is a batch process which can only be done periodically. After the newly received information has been inverted, these new term data then have to be added to existing term data. This term by term posting of batches of data is a costly process. Uniterm and small optical coincidence systems do not require an extra step to attain inversion. However, larger optical coincidence systems do require term-by-term posting of the new data.

C. Arrangement for Store Access

When an information system permits a number of simultaneous searches it is a multiple access system.

We can provide for a number of simultaneous searches by placing a number of reading heads in parallel on the same tape, etc. This provides only limited increase in access and is of relatively little practical importance.

The type of access considered here is based on searching a small fraction of the store rather than searching the entire collection. Since each search involves a different section of the memory it is possible to make many searches or entries simultaneously and the search is much faster.

A search question is always defined in "terms,"

and "items" are the result of the search. In other words, the "search input" consists of terms; the "search output" consists of items. Thus a search for coincidence of terms A and B, when performed on the inverted grouping system shown in Fig. 17, can be performed by comparing all item numbers grouped under "A" against all item numbers grouped under "B." Such a search involves only a fraction of the total store and leaves all the other terms free for other simultaneous searches. A large number of clerks may be entering new data while these searches go on. In other words, the store features multiple access.

On the other hand, if such a search were to be performed on the conventional grouping system of Fig. 13, the entire store of index data would have to be searched. This type of store, therefore, has Single Access. A collection arranged item by item in a single linear array, for example, on a single tape, is a single access system.

It is often necessary to "batch" questions in such systems in order to reduce search time. In this manner many searches can be performed simultaneously, but this practice delays answering of questions.

Multiple access is of great economic importance in mechanizing large information collections, for the following reason: Small collections of, for example, 10,000 items may not have more than, for example, ten questions a day, allowing about 8/10ths of an hour per search. However, if the collections grow to

108

1,000,000 items, we can expect at least 1,000 questions a day. Thus 100 times as many items will have to be searched in 1/100th of the same time. In other words, the search speed will have to go up by the factor 100^2 or 10,000.

Thus the main problem in the mechanization of large information collections is the problem of meeting the heavy search and data-entry loads required of such systems where thousands of searches a day and thousands of entries a day will not be uncommon.

Efficient ways of obtaining multiple access may well be the key to the problem of mechanizing the searching of large collections.

The above discussion should not lead to the conclusion that all item-grouped systems feature single access and all term-grouped systems feature multiple access. In practice this is not the case. Term-grouped systems may lose their multiple access and become single access systems when they are completely automated, and item grouped systems in subject card catalogs permit multiple access.

An example of such a single-access system having inverted grouping could be visualized as an optical coincidence system where each of the term cards has been edge coded at its bottom edge with its term, and where all of these cards have been placed at random in an Electrofile-type selection apparatus. A keyboard is used to select the term cards required for search. The keyboard makes the system a single-access system. This form of mechanization added to the optical coincidence system might, therefore, have more disadvantages than advantages (see Fig. 27).

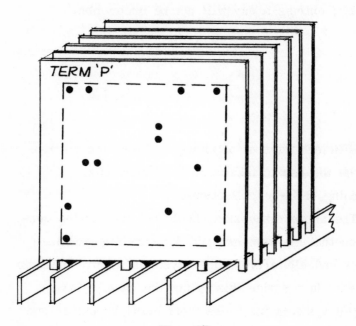

Fig. 27
Inverted Grouping
Simultaneous Scanning
Single Access

If each item were indexed by only one term, it would be easy to break up a conventionally-grouped collection in order to achieve multiple access. However, one-term indexing is practically never found. In dividing a conventional grouping collection by terms, an item of information indexed, for example, by ten different terms, must be "filed under each of these terms." If all items are indexed by ten terms, this would amount to tenfold multiplication of the total memory. Thus "memory multiplication" is the price that has to be paid for multiple access with conventional grouping. This type of index is also known as a subdivided index.

Despite this multiplication of memory the search speed is increased considerably. If a system has 1,000 terms, and each item of index information has to be filed under ten different terms, the search speed will be increased by a factor of one hundred. This will be purchased at the expense of a ten-fold increase in size of the file.

As all multiple access systems require each item to be "filed" under each of its index terms, and since every access term has a different physical location, this increases the entry labor and thus increases the cost of multiple-access systems with conventional grouping. Inverted grouping requires that the item code be posted under each of its index terms while conventional grouping requires filing the entire index information of each item under each of the item's index terms.

The best known example of this multiple-access conventional-grouping system is the Minicard system.[8] The Minicard system also features sequential matching (Fig. 28). Minicards carry search data and the complete document in microform. It is, of course, possible to use tape instead of unit records for the same logic utilized in the Minicard system.

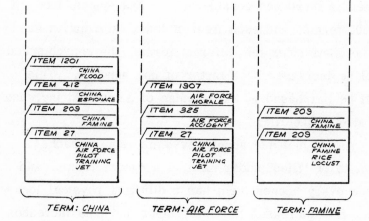

Fig. 28

Conventional Grouping
Sequential Scanning
Multiple Access

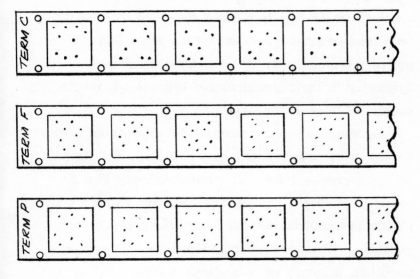

Fig. 29

Inverted Grouping
Simultaneous Matching
Multiple Access

Miniaturization of optical coincidence system. Each
frame is the image of a card of Fig. 25. Tapes are
based on 35 mm film, and are open ended. Search
by physical superimposition of term tapes, and frame-
by-frame scanning.

The earlier observation that inverted grouping
lends itself better to multiple access than does conventional grouping is based on the fact that any system is always entered by a question phrased in

"terms" (as input) and yields "items" (as output). If we wanted to enter a system by "items" to obtain "terms" as output search results, the inverted grouping would require memory-multiplication. Conventional grouping would then lend itself better to multiple access than inverted grouping. Thus while there is an inherent symmetry in these devices, there is a basic symmetry in their practical use because we always search by "terms" for "items."

As shown above, access is not an abstract design consideration like grouping and matching, but depends on the degree and form of mechanization. For all practical purposes, however, it appears to be a completely independent variable, just like grouping and matching. It should be considered one of the most important parameters of systems design.

It appears that the design considerations of grouping, matching and access are the most important considerations in machine design.

Since each of these three considerations has at least two possible values, all possible information storage and retrieval devices belong to one of 2^3 or 8 possible basic systems. These eight basic systems are shown in Fig. 22.

In practice there is a wide variety of machines. The reason for this is that each of the basic systems may be modified by a number of other considerations, such as coding and structural principles.

Secondary Design Considerations

A. Coding Principles

All I. R. systems may be based on one of two coding principles. One principle is "direct" or "non-superimposed" coding. This means that every term is encoded in a separate coding field. The other principle is "superimposed" coding, in which terms are encoded upon each other in the same coding field.

Direct coding has the advantage that it is possible to recall and completely print out the index data from the memory. In principle, this makes it possible to perform tabulations, listings and statistical and other accounting processes automatically.

This is not possible with superimposed coding because the terms, when superimposed, lose their identity. All superimposed coding yields is the serial numbers, or addresses, of the selected items. Superimposed coding may also yield a number of spurious, unwanted addresses.

This advantage of direct coding is frequently bought at the cost of complicated automatic search equipment. Where indexing is performed by only a small number of fixed mutually exclusive classes, such as sex, age, wage-class, education, etc. the required circuitry is fairly simple, since each term has a dedicated position. When indexing by non-exclusive classes, the field in which a term is encoded is unknown. In order to search for coincidence of terms, each term must be compared with all of the index terms of each document. Larger amounts of complicated electronic circuitry and memory elements are, therefore, required.

On the other hand, superimposed coding makes possible some relatively simple and inexpensive search procedures and devices, such as the Zator[9] system or the Alpha-Optical Coincidence[6] system based on cards dedicated to letters of the alphabet.

Each of these two major coding systems, may be divided into subsystems, each of which may, in principle, be applied to each of the eight basic machine systems. The same is true of the various structural modification which can be utilized in all of these possible systems.

B. Structural Considerations

Form of "Bit"

An important structural consideration is the physical structure of the information "bit" used in coding. The word "bit" is here used loosely to mean the physical element which contains the bit.

In the movable memories we will distinguish only between the permanent form of bit and the change-of-state form of bit. Permanent information bits are holes in cards or tapes, or transparent spots on opaque records or magnetic ink spots.

Holes in cards or tapes are, broadly speaking, the cheapest form of information bit.

Photographic reduction permits very dense storage. A very attractive possibility of this form of bit is the performance of searches for coincidence of terms simply by superimposing records as in superimposable card systems (Fig. 25). One of the most attractive features of this form of bit for information retrieval purposes is its permanence or indestructibility (if indestructibility is desired).

Many types of change-of-state forms of bit usable with movable memories are possible. The only well-developed form of this type or bit is the magnetic spot. It is a non-permanent form of bit entailing some dangers of accidental loss of memory. For reading or writing, the read-write head is brought close to the record. It requires motion between the record and the read-write head. No searching by physical superimposition of records is possible.

Form of Record

Each of the above forms of bit may be used with each of the many possible forms of record. The most important forms of records are card, tapes, discs, and drums. Each of these has its own advantages and drawbacks.

Cards. Given the same type of bit and the same density, cards generally allow densest storage (in bits per cubic foot) and the lowest cost (in cost per bit).

Tapes. Again, given the same type of bit and the same density, tapes form the second most dense form of storage. Generally speaking, only tapes and cards have so far proven acceptable for I.R. purposes.

Discs. For the same type of bit, discs have less dense storage but more rapid access than tapes. They seem to form an ideal compromise between these two requirements, for accounting, inventory control and similar applications. As a "store" for information retrieval purposes the cost is extremely high.

Drums. For the same type of bit, drums provide the lowest storage density (in bits per cubic foot) but the best access, both in speed, as well as possible number of reading heads. For these reasons it is favored as an intermediate speed memory for high-speed computers. The high cost per bit precludes application as a "store" for information retrieval purposes.

C. Micro-Photographic Document Storage

The Rapid Selector [11,12] was the first true information storage and retrieval system built specifically for these purposes.

Only in special cases should combination of the "finding mechanism" and micro-photographic document storage be considered. The cost and the constraints this imposes upon the system are so great that careful justification will be required.

Summation of Examples of 8 Basic Systems
(see also Fig. 21)

1. Inverted Grouping, Simultaneous Matching, Multiple Access

   Examples: "Uniterm" systems (Fig. 18)[2]

   Optical Coincidence Systems (Fig. 20)[6]

   Miniaturized optical coincidence systems (Fig. 29)[6]

2. Inverted Grouping, Simultaneous Matching, Single Access

   Examples: "Uniterm" systems, optical coincidence systems with automatic term selection (see Fig. 27)

   Alpha optical coincidence systems[6]

3. Inverted Grouping, Linear Matching, Multiple Access

   Examples: Systems based on optical coincidence tapes, with manual selection of tapes (Fig. 26)

   Punched card collating systems, among which is the IBM "Special Index Analyzer"[13]

4. Inverted Grouping, Linear Matching, Single Access

   Examples: Many computers search according to this logic. Instead of having a separate tape for each term, all terms and the posting under these terms are on one or only a few tapes[5]

The Disc-memory type computers when used for I.R. purposes could also best be classified in this manner.

The Magnacard system operates best according to this logic[16]

5. Conventional Grouping, Simultaneous Matching, Multiple Access

Examples: System of Fig. 28 with a selection device as shown in Fig. 24[7] for each term

6. Conventional Grouping, Simultaneous Matching, Single Access

Examples: Card selection systems as shown in Fig. 24

"Electrofile" system[7]

"McBee-Keysort[3]

"Zator" system[9]

7. Conventional Grouping, Linear Matching, Multiple Access

Examples: "Minicard" system (Fig. 28)[8]

Conventional Library Card catalog

Such a system can also be based on the use of punched card scanners or card scanning computers.[4]

8. Conventional Grouping, Linear Matching, Single Access

Examples: G.E. Search Comparator[15]

The "Rapid Selector"[11, 12, 14]

F.M.A.'s "Filesearch"[14]

Herner & Company's "Tape Searcher[17]

Punched card scanners[4]

Western Reserve University's system, now superseded by G.E. 225 general purpose computer.

Many computers use this logic[5]

(Basic Principles of I.R. Devices)

References*

1. In preparing these references, names of manufacturers of equipment have in all instances been
given. For well known and long established systems, such as punched card systems and edge
notched card systems, going back long before
World War II, no literature references have been
given since these references would be outdated and
superseded by commercial literature, which is
extremely comprehensive and instructive.

For general purpose computers no literature
references have been given for the same reason
and because of the prohibitive volume.

For newer special I.R. devices, literature references have been given where available.

2. Taube, Mortimer, "Studies in Coordinate Indexing," Documentation, Inc., Bethesda, Md.

3. Edge notched card systems are commercially
available from the following companies: Royal
McBee Corporation (Keysort system) and Shaw
Walker Corporation (Easy Sort System).

4. Punched card systems, Hollerith systems or com-
parable systems are commercially available from
the following companies: General Electric Corporation, IBM Corporation, R.C.A. and Remington
Rand Corporation. Abroad systems of this nature
are manufactured by Bull and Samas.

5. Information retrieval on magnetic tape can be practiced on practically all of the general purpose electronic computer systems. Major manufacturers of computers include: Autonetics, Bendix, Burroughs, Control Data Corporation, General Electric, General Precision, Honeywell Corporation, IBM, National Cash Register Corporation, Philco Corporation, R.C.A., Remington Rand and Scientific Data Systems.

6. Optical coincidence devices are commercially available from: Jonker Business Machines, Inc. (Termatrex and Minimatrex systems). See also: Jonker, Frederick, the new "Termatrex" Line of I.R. Systems--The "Minimatrex" Line of I.R. systems, Am Doc, 14 No. 4 (1963)

7. The Electrofile system is commercially available from the A.C.M.E. Visible Record Company. Only company literature available.

8. The Minicard system is commercially available from the Eastman Kodak Company. See also: Kipers, J.W., Tyler, A.W. and Myers, W.L., "A Minicard System for Documentating Information," Am Doc, 8, No. 4: 246-68.

9. The Zator system is commercially available from the Zator Corporation, 140 1/2 Mt. Auburn St., Boston, Mass. See also: Mooers, Calvin N., "Zato Coding Applied to Mechanical Organization of Knowledge," Am Doc, 2, No. 1.

10. "Total Data Processing," Am Data Proc, 4: 43-6 (April, 1962).

11. McMurray, James P., "The Bureau of Ships Rapid Selector System," Am Doc, 13, No. 1: 66-8 (Jan., 1962).

12. Bush, Vannevar, "As We May Think," Atlantic Monthly, 176: 101-8 (July, 1945).

13. Taube, Mortimer, "The Comac, An Efficient

Punched Card Collating System for Information Storage and Retrieval," International Conference on Scientific Information, 2, National Academy of Sciences, Washington, D.C.

14. The Filesearch is commercially available from FMA, Inc., El Segundo, California. See also: "FMA Filesearch," Records Management (July, 1962).

15. The "Search Comparator" is commercially available from the General Electric Information Systems Operation, Bethesda, Maryland. Only company literature available.

16. Magnacard systems are commercially available from the Magnavox Company. See also: Laurent, R.L., "Magnavox Information Storage and Retrieval Systems." Presented at Los Angeles Chapter of American Documentation Institute. Reprints available from Magnavox Research Labs, 2829 Maricopa Street, Torrance, California.

17. Under development by Herner & Company, Washington, D.C. Only company literature available.